PSYCHOLOGICAL FIRST AID

Eva Roman

2000

Copyright © Eva Roman 2005

All rights reserved. No part of this publication may be reproduced, stored in a retrieval
system, or transmitted in any form or by any means, electronic, mechanical, photocopying,
recording, or otherwise without the prior permission of the publishers.

First published in 2005 by Management Books 2000 Ltd
Forge House, Limes Road
Kemble, Cirencester
Gloucestershire, GL7 6AD, UK
Tel: 0044 (0) 1285 771441
Fax: 0044 (0) 1285 771055
E-mail: mb2000@btconnect.com
Web: www.mb2000.com

Printed and bound in Great Britain by Digital Books Logistics Ltd of Peterborough

This book is sold subject to the condition that it shall not, by way of trade or otherwise,
be lent, resold, hired out, or otherwise circulated without the publisher's prior consent in any
form of binding or cover other than that in which it is published and without a similar
condition including this condition being imposed upon the subsequent purchaser.

British Library Cataloguing in Publication Data is available
ISBN 1-85252-475-8

Contents

Acknowledgements

My grateful thanks go to Dr Raymond D. Shelton, Ph.D. of the American Academy for Experts in Traumatic Stress for giving me permission to use some material from their substantial research which has been carried out since 9/11.

Thanks also for the information which has been made available from some of the caring organisations and used widely by counsellors treating people suffering from Traumatic Stress.

I have also drawn on some of my own publications which include Trauma, co-authored with Roger Barnet, First Aid in the Workplace and Recruitment and Selection

Introduction

Psychological First Aid is one of the most essential primary support systems after a critical incident has taken place. This may be due to a major disaster such as a train crash, affecting many passengers and staff who become casualties or an industrial incident which not only causes danger to human lives but can also shock or often traumatise onlookers who witnessed the accident.

Those who receive serious injuries will be looked after by emergency services or any qualified First Aiders who may be available. However, as soon as news of the incident leaks out, the scene very quickly becomes littered with people willing to lend a hand.

This is very commendable in most cases but what is often seriously missing is the expertise required to respond with proper knowledge of the kind of support victims require immediately after the incident.

The chaotic scenes often created are due to a total lack of training and co-ordination of what is required and where victims who are mobile should be guided to in order to be given support.

The general public, although very keen to help, unfortunately only add to the chaos and confusion by cluttering up space and getting in the way, which will be needed by the emergency services in order to transport casualties into ambulances in an attempt to try and save lives.

Not everyone involved in the incident will become traumatised. However, the immediate shock after a critical incident is bound to leave many people, including bystanders, in a very disturbed frame of mind, unable to concentrate on important issues related to their immediate needs which may even include minor injuries which the victim has failed to notice. .

Psychological First Aid does not consist of on the spot counselling the victim. The carer is required to become a 'prop' and, apart from shielding affected individuals from further harm, needs to attend to their immediate pressing needs which may involve matters relating to business, such as attending meetings, home life or children. Any minor physical injuries will also require attention. There are many interrelated aspects to observe and deal with when rendering Psychological First Aid.

In the business world, careful consideration has to be given to the task of choosing someone to perform the task of dealing with cases in a critical incident. There is very little point in taking a subjective view in recruiting people who seem to be suitable candidates because they have a sympathetic nature, without first preparing a job description and personnel specification which identifies essential as well as desirable characteristics. This task requires a scientific approach. Although people may have worked for the organisation for quite some time and may seem very suitable, information about their skills will apply to their technical abilities which may not match with their human skills.

The personnel or human resources department staff would be required to draw up a recruitment list for suitable candidates which can then be circulated around the organisation to staff considered suitable for the task of looking after the needs of possible victims in a critical incident. It will only become clear after studying the applications and during interviews whether there are hidden characteristics which render some employees totally unsuitable for such a post.

Once a team has been chosen, a suitable training programme will need to be designed and organised which will have to be administered by a fully qualified and experienced specialist in this area.

Apart from the subject of the psychology of human behaviour and the different stages of support, it is essential that candidates are trained in emergency First Aid so that casualties can be treated as required.

Traumatic reactions can produce many different characteristics and carers will benefit from the knowledge and recognition of these symptoms, which will enable them to put Psychological First Aid into place without time wastage.

It may well seem that there are people who do not appear to be affected by a critical incident at the impact stage. However, reactions may occur after a period of time which will necessitate providing more advanced methods of support. In turn, this will require more qualified counsellors to take over the support which may well include further attention for the carers, who may develop psychological reactions to the incident.

The following chapters provide detailed guidelines on recruitment and selection procedures for those people who decide to render Psychological First Aid to victims of critical incidents. It leads the reader through all the required procedures necessary and the characteristics needed by the carer to provide support to anyone suffering from reactions to a traumatic incident. The latest First Aid requirements and procedures recommended by Health and Safety Executive are described, and a chapter is devoted to 'Taking Care of the Carer'.

These guidelines can be applied to people wishing to become carers in the workplace as well as those who wish to give support to victims at home or in public places.

PART ONE

Choosing the right carer

Characteristics of a suitable carer

Drawing up a job description

Personnel specifications

Designing a suitable application form

Organisation of training

1

Choosing the Right Carer

From the many incidents I have attended, only very few were dealt with by people who had received the proper training to deal with such situations.

Most of these were concerned with physical First Aid requirements but, as times change, psychological needs are as important as physical injuries. However, knowledge of how to deal with the immediate shock and consequent needs during such incidents is sadly lacking.

It is a well known fact that as soon as a major incident has taken place either in the workplace or in public places or even at home, the 'do-gooders' race to the scene and attempt to give assistance. All they achieve in many situations, is to add to the chaos which has taken place.

Numerous things need to be dealt with but, above all, even those casualties who are not badly injured are nevertheless seriously affected by the shock of the situation and will experience traumatic reactions. This means that they will not be able to deal with important issues which need to be tackled in the immediate future. These might include fetching offspring from school or child-minders, finding alternative accommodation due to destruction of their home or many other reasons which may even include theft, attack or assault.

A gentle hand is often missing at this point as the do-gooders may well have adverse reactions themselves and it quickly becomes clear that neither the victim nor the person attempting to help is capable of dealing sensibly with the situation.

At such a time, many things require the right approach and the choice of the right person to carry out this support will have to be made with great care if they are to take over this task in the workplace. Those who are willing to give assistance outside the workplace would be strongly advised to seek training at a suitable venue.

The business of recruiting suitable personnel in the workplace must be carried out with the same care and approach as is applied to personnel required for technical or managerial positions. Since recruiting one or more carers will be done from within the company and from existing staff, it will be necessary to employ the same method which would be used if full time staff was required.

Since carers would only be required to perform this duty if a critical incident took place and would have to leave the job they normally performed for a time, recruitment of such support staff should not be based on intuition or experience alone. The person who shows great ability in technical skills may be totally unsuitable to look after victims who have been affected by adverse reactions due to a critical incident – for numerous reasons.

A little thought will reveal that generally the intuitive type of recruitment procedure must be unsatisfactory for assessing the suitability of candidates for support jobs. Although most people like to think they are good at judging people's abilities and personalities, the fact is that some are better at it than others. Like any other ability, this particular skill is possessed in different amounts by different people. Also, a person who is reputedly good at judging others is not necessarily good at selecting people for jobs. One learns from every-day contacts and experiences to judge people from the point of view of their value to oneself and this can interfere with the ability to make an objective assessment of their job suitability. Appearance, for example, can frequently be the cause of a candidate's acceptance or rejection, yet a specific appearance is rarely needed for successful performance in a job.

It is hoped that the candidates for this additional job will all have been through a scientific and systematic recruitment procedure for their existing job, which takes into account all the information required to give and get as detailed a profile of the job requirements as is possible. The interview, for example can be expected to throw light upon intellectual and social skills, personal energy, motivation, technical knowledge and experience and the type and degree of development of interests. To add to this information, it will be necessary to investigate how the prospective carer might stand up to emotional pressure, the need for fast decisions to be made, additional and perhaps disturbing sights and the ability to take charge of abnormal situations.

In the case of carers in the workplace, general forms may well already be in use. However, as this is an additional job outside the recruitment procedures normally applied, specific forms may have to be designed, such as a short description of the requirements which can be handed to people who are thought to be suitable for this position. Application forms will also have different questions to be answered, for example knowledge or qualifications in First Aid, befriending skills in order to establish a fast rapport, listening skills, communication skills and above all, practical skills.

There is a very strong case *against* selecting people already employed by an organisation, who appear to have a sympathetic nature. Maybe, in a situation requiring assistance at minor accidents, such a person selected as apparently suitable to become a carer has a negative reaction to dealing with heavy bleeding. Such support requires a cool approach, and panic or worse would be totally unsuitable in cases of disaster.

In order to gain additional information about the candidate, it is necessary to prepare beforehand a description of the essential characteristics of the person or persons being sought so that the interviewer can keep this accessible whilst assessing the candidates. Interviewers can also attempt to make themselves aware of their own prejudices and limitations so that they do not unduly affect judgements.

With all the information already on record related to the candidates and the very valuable additional details which mainly deal with the human aspects of the prospective carer, decisions for job placements, based on an objective, systematic recruitment approach will become much more successful.

2

Characteristics of a Suitable Carer

There are certain behavioural elements which are essential adjuncts to performing the role of supplying psychological First Aid. The carer will in most cases be the first person on the scene after a critical incident has taken place. Often there will be frightened, dazed and shocked people, either too stunned to move in any direction or trying to run from the horror just witnessed. There will also be those whose reaction will be to reject any support and even become aggressive.

Whichever reaction a survivor shows, it requires careful handling on the part of the carer, who must possess certain essential and desirable qualities and characteristics which should be established when when recruiting people for this support role.

The following information could be incorporated into a short description of what this job entails and the requirements for it which will give possible applicants some idea and choice regarding suitability. It will also be helpful in preparing an application form which will undoubtedly differ from the normal form used by the organisation.

● **Ability to take control**
   The person who takes responsibility for a survivor requires a sufficiently strong personality to be able to take charge of the situation and recognise what the immediate needs are for that person.

● **Common sense**
   There will be certain requirements which need to be attended to

17

in sequence, depending on the condition of the survivor and the general situation concerning the scene of the incident.

● Calmness

A survivor may well become agitated or even hysterical but will be encouraged to develop trust in the carer's ability to help if the carer remains calm and in control.

● Empathy

The carer needs to recognise the difference between empathy and sympathy. Feeling sorry for a survivor can have adverse reactions and might even to suggest to that person that things are much worse than they actually are. Empathy shows that the carer is able to experience the survivor's feelings and show this.

● Providing safety

The carer must assess the situation and, if necessary move the survivor to a place of safety as quickly as possible but keeping the person informed at all times what the carer intends to do.

● Listening

The ability to listen to the needs of the survivor is essential so that important issues can be dealt with. The survivor will undoubtedly worry about the tasks they cannot perform at this time and paying attention to the survivor's requests will put their minds at ease.

● Communication

An exchange of information between the carer and the survivor in a simple but clear manner will help to establish the important tasks which need to be carried out.

● Problem Solving

The carer should possess good problem-solving attributes since the survivor will not be in a fit state after a critical incident to think clearly or make decisions of a problematic nature.

● **Non-argumentative**

It is important to avoid arguments with survivors as this will increase their anxiety and encourage them to mistrust the carer, thus making assistance more difficult.

● **Reassurance**

The carer needs to have the ability to give as much re-assurance as possible but refrain from giving exaggerated information which may not be truthful.

● **Honesty**

Should there be any problems which cannot be solved at the time, which my require assistance from more qualified staff, the carer should refrain from keeping such information from the survivor but give facts in a caring manner.

The above are by no means all the characteristics required for becoming a carer and rendering Psychological First Aid but they indicate some of the necessary behavioural attributes needed to deal with critical incident survivors.

3

Drawing up a Job Description

Serious incidents occur from time to time in any organisation and either people are injured or those nearest to the scene of the incident are forced to view disturbing scenes or are even drawn into the aftermath of possible serious injuries to colleagues, perhaps through industrial accidents or any number of critical incidents where help and support is required.

In many cases, a trained support team of carers is not available to deal with those who are affected by the incident which has occurred and this may cause more chaos than is needed at such a critical time when time may be of the essence.

Not everyone is suitable to provide such support and it requires carefully chosen staff to become a carer if such situations arise. This means either Personnel or Human Resources executives need to go through a process of recruitment. The choice for such support staff will obviously come from suitable existing employees. However, due to the nature of the job and the requirements on a part-time or occasional basis which will only have to be carried out in cases of need, a specific job description and personnel specification will have to be drawn up. However, just because it is an occasional support job which will take people away from their regular occupation does not mean that only intuitive choices should be made to obtain the right people to act as carers.

Thus, right at the beginning, a scientific approach to the filling of vacancies differs from the intuitive approach. It begins with the preparation of a systematic, factual and concise description of the job, which is then translated into behavioural terms to provide a specification or profile of the type of person most likely to carry out the job most successfully. At selection, the candidates whose profiles make the best match with this specification will be offered the position of carers dealing with Psychological First Aid in any emergency

In order to design a specific job description for the position of carers for survivors who have been involved in or have witnessed a critical incident, special preparations have to be put into practice. People involved in recruitment and selection sometimes argue that all this preparation is a waste of time when a particular job has similarities. But it is only when the facts about a job have been collected and analysed that it becomes obvious how relatively unique the particular job is. The best way to complete a job description systematically is to use a checklist while describing the work. This ensures important points are covered and makes for economy of time and thought. The main headings suitable for describing a carer's job are:

1   General information about the organisation and the job

2. Outline of work done

3. Selection and training

4. Working conditions which are divided into:
     a) Physical working conditions
     b) Social working conditions
     c) Economic working conditions

5. Prospects of transfer and promotion

The information collected under these headings will be concerned with the exact duties of the job, the training needed, the conditions under which the work is done and, most important, the responsibilities, satisfactions and emergency demands which may not be apparent at first glance. A great deal of attention must be paid to facts like overlooking or minimising the difficulties of the job or giving a false impression of some kind. Special attention must be paid to what people consider are the disagreeable or difficult features of the job which, in this case may well be the possible psychological reactions of the carer if insufficient training is given prior to commencement.

Checklist for Job Description

1. **General**
   a. Name and place of work
   b. Number of employees
   c. Age range

2. **Outline of work done**
   a. Contents of work
   b. Duties and responsibilities

3. **Selection and training**
   a. Methods of selection
   b. Probationary period, if any
   c. Training after entry: initial, upgrading, where obtained, period

4. **Working conditions**
   a. Physical conditions of work: location, general physical conditions, working hours, accuracy required, variety, any disagreeable features
   b. Social conditions of work: size and nature of immediate working group, amount of companionship, team or individual process, amount of supervision, welfare facilities, debriefing facilities
   c. Economic conditions of work: (monthly, weekly, hourly), range of pay (starting, increments, maximum), sickness benefits

5. **Opportunities for transfer and promotion**
   a. To work within the organisation
   b. In similar organisations,
   c. In related fields

Note: These items do not necessarily exhaust all the possibilities.

The following is a suggested ideal requirements list which can be adapted to suit the organisational requirements when drawing up details required for a carer's position.

1. First Aid qualifications
2. Organisational abilities
3. Fluency in communications
4. Ability to assess trauma reactions
5. Ability to deal with emotional or aggressive survivors
6. Common sense approach towards disaster victims
7. Leadership characteristics
8. Ability to give orders with authority
9. Ability to write clear and concise reports of actions taken

The above job suggestions can be added to or altered to achieve a tailored description, according to requirements. There is no specific rule which states that carers must be male or female. This will be related to the type of work being carried out within the organisation.

It is often found that the most sensible approach is to recruit an equal number of male and female carers, depending on the size of the company, since victims of trauma often feel more comfortable with someone of the same sex as themselves and will relate better to them.

4

Personnel Specification

Up until now the investigator will have been describing the job and this must be kept separate from the next stage, that of preparing the Personnel Specification. Various Institutes issuing recommendations for recruitment and selection claim that a common fault of people when they first describe the work for selection purposes is to think immediately in terms of rather abstract human attributes such as *'necessary clarity of speech'* instead of describing what the person actually has to do. There is a lot of difference, for example, between effective long-distance telephoning and trying to communicate with a survivor who has just been involved in a critical incident, who is very shocked and requires help and support in practical matters. To say that *'clarity of speech'* is required in both cases, with no further qualifications could result in very different kinds of work appearing to be closely similar. Use of a checklist can help the investigator to avoid falling into this kind of trap.

To indicate how the personnel specification is prepared, reference is made to the Seven-point Plan of the National Institute of Industrial Psychology. The plan also provides a suitable framework within which to conduct the interviews, thereby facilitating the task of comparing candidates' profiles with the specification.

The main headings of the specification, as provided by the plan are:

- Physical make-up
- Attainments
- General intelligence
- Special aptitudes

- Interests
- Disposition
- Circumstances

What must now be completed is an interpretation of the facts contained in the job description in the light of these headings. Under *'physical make-up'*, for example, what does the job demand in the way of general health, physical stamina,. hearing, vision and manner. Under the heading *'disposition,'*, do the duties of the job demand that the person should be steady, dependable, persevering, persistent, show a great deal of empathy, able to get on well with others, or what?

The Institute points out that when interpreting the job factors, it is essential to keep in mind the methods by which candidates' potentialities are likely to be assessed. Ill-defined requirements, which will not be revealed by interview, psychological tests or past records, must be avoided. The meaning of such terms as 'needs the highest moral integrity' is hard to determine. In the short time usually available, it is difficult to assess such qualities as industriousness, which is often erroneously thought to colour a whole personality, but tends to show up in one set of circumstances and not in another.

It is also essential to realise that the importance attached to certain requirements will vary and it is always necessary to distinguish clearly, possibly by using a grading system, between the minimum standard normally required in a certain respect and the standard that would be desirable. This helps to avoid wasting ability, or over-estimating the difficulties of finding suitable candidates because the additional work is thought to require greater ability than it needs. A distinction should also be made between *essential* requirements, without which the job cannot be performed to a satisfactory standard and *desirable* requirements. A list of essential requirements helps to reject candidates; a list of desirable requirements helps to rank in order the candidates who match up to the essential requirements.

Since candidates already employed by the organisation will be asked to apply for the post of providing psychological first aid, personnel will have detailed records from previous recruitment campaigns. However, the job of providing care to survivors of critical incidents requires characteristics not previously required in the job they are currently carrying out. Therefore it is essential to review and alter any standard forms used so that they apply to the new support cover with its many psychological attributes needed to carry out the job of a carer.

Personnel Specification

Essential   Desirable

1. **Physical Make-up**
   a. Age
   b. Functioning: health record, vision, hearing, ability to work under particular conditions
   c. Appearance: cleanliness, smartness, etc
   d. Bearing: posture, vigour, etc
   e. Speech: quality, accent, etc

2. **Attainments and previous experience**
   a. General education & scholastic achievements
   b. Occupational training and certificates obtained
   c. Relevant experience: type of work, length and level of responsibility, etc

3. **General intelligence**
   The level, in relation to the relevant occupational population, required to do the job:
   a. satisfactorily
   b. well

4. **Special aptitudes**
   Any special ability, other than that provided by General intelligence, or indicated by competence or interest in, for example, knowledge of first aid

5. **Occupational or leisure interests**
   The degree to which the job requires interest in:
   a. The intellectual sphere – solving problems of an administrative nature

	Essential	Desirable

   b. The social sphere – persuading, managing,
       understanding, helping, or being with people

6. Disposition
   Job requirements:
   a. Being steady, dependable, persevering, persistent,
       even tenacious, being difficult to distract or to
       to discourage
   b. Getting on well with others, working readily with
       others, co-operating
   c. Influencing others easily and effectively
   d. Depending on him/herself rather than others, relying
       on own resources, accepting responsibility

7. Circumstances
   a. Is any special background helpful?
   b. How committed should the successful applicant be
       in his/her domestic circumstances?

8. Contra-indications
   What attributes would automatically exclude candidates
   who in other respects meet the specification?

The personnel specification is an extremely important tool in helping to recruit carers in the event of a disaster happening in the work place. While the job description describes the type of work the carer will be expected to carry out, the personnel specification is able to give a detailed account of the candidate's characteristics and attributes needed to support those who have just been involved in or have witnessed a critical incident.

The personnel specification shown can of course be adjusted to suit the person being selected which will be discussed in part two of this book. As mentioned earlier, there will be some characteristics which are desirable and some which are essential. With a person specification such as the one shown, the details can be adjusted as the organisation demands, by identifying and qualifying each element, in the right-hand columns.

5

The Application Form

Most organisations have at least one application form for the recruitment of new staff which has been specifically designed to suit the company and to obtain as much information as possible for a suitable candidate.

In this instance, the candidates required for the job of carer in case of critical incidents will be recruited from within the organisation and therefore details will already be on file about applicants who wish to take on this support role. However, since this job does not require any of the technical skills which staff were originally employed to do, a carefully thought out application form can serve a number of useful purposes. At the application stage, comparison is made easier if applicants complete a form that asks them all the same questions. Selectors can then more easily decide which applicants they wish to reject at this stage and which they wish to call for interview.

At the interview, information on the form indicates areas which, in the applicant's present position, have not been explored or even required and, depending on its design, the form may allow space for interview notes. In the case of successful candidates, information on the form can be transferred to already existing personnel records.

Whatever the number of purposes served by the application forms of an organisation, however, they should always make it easier for applicants to apply and should continue the organisation image-building which, in the first instance began with an advertisement. Internal recruitment is usually advertised by placing information about the job requirements in prominent places around the organisation or by providing information sheets to all members of staff and requesting those interested to ask for an application form. Normally an application form will be divided into five sections:

- personal information (name, address, date of birth etc)
- education
- occupational history
- recreational pursuits
- space for any additional information the applicant may wish to give.

The questions in each section will depend on what basic information is required to assist selection for the vacancy concerned. For example, with regard to the candidate's occupational history, both in the job description and personnel specification, essential and desirable attributes need to be clearly stated – in this case, a qualification in First Aid would be required.

A question that may be too narrowly defined is the one requesting hobbies and interests. This wording may cause an applicant to leave out important information – sporting activities, for instance, which some people do not classify under either heading. A better wording of the question could be:

What are your main interests and what other things do you do in your spare time?

The effectiveness of an application form can be assessed by carrying out certain checks, for example:

- the number of forms returned from those sent out
- the number of occasions when applicants have insufficient space to answer particular questions
- the number of times the additional information section produced the same evidence which, for comparison purposes, it would be better to obtain by question on the form
- the number of times a question is misunderstood, indicating that it needs to be reworded or more clearly defined.

When considering whether it would be worthwhile to attempt assessment of the form's effectiveness, it should be remembered that the true cost of a procedure is often the cost of using the form, not the production cost.

The following list is a detailed sample of the five sections contained in an application form for the post of carer in the event of a critical incident. These contents, to be provided by the applicant in addition to those already on file should contain information related to aptitudes required for this support role.

Application Form – Possible items to be covered

1. **Personal Information**
   a. Name
   b. Address
   c. Home telephone number
   d. Date and place of birth
   e. Sex, marital status, dependents – children and others
   f. Height, weight, state of health generally, and specifically with regard to occupational requirements
   g. Relations employed by the organisation
   h. Father's occupation
   i. Occupation of brothers and sisters

2. **Education**
   a. General: schools attended: name and type; examinations taken: subjects, grades, dates; offices held; scholarships, prizes, school activities
   b. Further college/university: name, period of attendance; examinations taken: subjects, grades, dates; offices held; extra curricular activities
   c. Vocational training: nature and place of training, period, period; professional qualifications: subjects taken, dates

3. **Occupational history**
   a. Chronological record of jobs held with dates
   b. Duties and responsibilities of each job and to whom responsible

   c. Names and addresses of previous employers
   d. Wages or salary for each job and reasons for leaving
   e. Names and addresses of referees

4. Recreational pursuits
   a. Hobbies – sporting and other activities
   b. Responsible positions held – e.g. team captain, chairman of debating society or secretary of club

5. General
   a. Dates and times would be available for interview
   b. Date free to commence in additional position (carer)

The reason for providing potential applicants with further details of the additional job is to assist these people to decide whether they are suited to the job, to any training that may be required and to the emotional and sometimes physical stresses involved in such support work. They can then eliminate themselves if they are not suited, which saves the organisation time and expense in dealing with them further. The information sheet provides a first screening, but as only key factors appear, these details – based more extensively on the job description/personnel specification – help to ensure that the response is reduced to the required compact quality field of applicants.

6

Organisation of Training

Once the choice of carers has been made, which largely depends on the size of the organisation, whether it is an industrial or commercial workplace and, above all whether the general public may be involved, for example in a shopping mall or a town centre, a training programme will have to be provided before disaster strikes.

A successful business depends on its employees being able to perform job tasks to the best of their ability and in a safe and healthy working environment.

Many businesses are now aware of the harmful impact trauma can have on employees and their performance at work and are putting into place measures to lessen the risks.

It makes economic sense to plan, equip and provide an effective and rapid response to a critical incident. Doing nothing can be extremely costly in terms of absenteeism, employees' long term health and loss of business productivity.

The recruitment of carers will also give the organisation the opportunity to review their Crisis Intervention Plan. The four areas which need to be looked at are:

1. **Crisis Preparation**
   a. Management Awareness Training to identify anxiety/stressors
   b. Interviewing and choosing a Crisis Response Team

2. **Crisis Management**
   a. Training at two levels;
      i) Management of Crisis Response Team (Management Awareness)

    ii) Training the Crisis Response Team (Peer
        Training) (including Psychological First Aid)

3. Crisis Response
    a. Post Traumatic Stress Reduction (psychological debriefing)
       (post incident)
    b. Review; 4/5 weeks after Trauma Reduction

4. Crisis Recovery
    a. On-going support counselling – up to 6 sessions (if required)
    b. Psychological Assessment
    c. Long-term counselling (if required)
    d. Group work (Trauma Support Groups)

The above plan can, of course be reduced, according to the size of the
organisation and also the number of people who may be traumatised
in any critical incident. It is however essential to put the carer's
training programme into operation and to draw up a procedural plan
so that everyone knows what they should be doing and where they
should be during an incident.

In order to provide Psychological First Aid, the new recruits
should attend a number of training sessions, beginning with some
guidelines of the reactions which can be experienced by victims or
bystanders after a critical incident. This subject need not be provided
in great detail as the carer is not required to give counselling on the
spot. Their role is that of a psychological prop who looks after the
initial reaction which besets those who were immediately involved.
However, this does not mean that others will not be affected, since the
after-effects of the traumatic incident can have what is known as a
'Ripple Effect' which is most potent in the centre, where casualties or
people nearest to the incident are at the time of impact. This will cause
a more violent reaction than to those who were on the edge of the
incident. Even someone who was not at the scene can have traumatic
reaction just by being told about the disaster. The following diagram
shows an example of the 'Ripple Effect'.

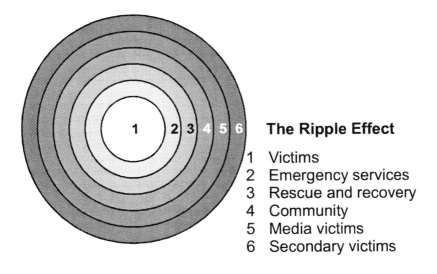

The Ripple Effect

1 Victims
2 Emergency services
3 Rescue and recovery
4 Community
5 Media victims
6 Secondary victims

Levels of Victims (after Frazer and Taylor 1981)

In order to give some idea to the prospective carer what they might find when called to a critical incident, the following gives an indication of what the survivor might display if the reaction is a *psychological* one and not a *physical injury*:

1. The person will be extremely shocked, may be trembling and also show signs of confusion. They may find it difficult to accept the situation

2. There is often a need to keep moving about, which produces disorientation.

3. People often experience fear of repetition of the incident. Anxiety related to personal safety and that of colleagues may be present

4. It may become apparent that the survivor will develop adverse feelings towards anyone and anything. They may even refuse help.

At this stage there is very little advantage to be gained by trying to persuade the person to follow instructions by telling them what to do. A caring attitude, showing empathy, will help to calm the person down, at which point the carer can begin to suggest ways of helping to carry out personal needs which the survivor is not capable of performing for him- or herself at this stage.

It is essential that the training programme includes instructions on First Aid. If the candidate has had previous training in this subject, management needs to find out how long ago this training took place as first aid methods frequently change. It is up to the organisation to decide whether the candidates undergo a full first aid course lasting four days, ending with an examination which gives them a qualification lasting three years or provide a one day emergency first aid course which deals with life threatening injuries or conditions. Such a course can be specifically designed, according to requirements.

The following is a suggested list of subjects which should be presented to the prospective carers which can be used as an introduction to trauma and Psychological First Aid.

Post Traumatic Stress Syndrome

1. **Introduction to post traumatic stress**
   What is trauma?

2. **Signs, symptoms and reactions**
   The recognition of post traumatic stress

3. **Trauma in the workplace**
   Group exploration of incidents

4. **Safety procedures**
   Dealing with the traumatised employee

5. **The debriefing process**
   Treatment after the incident

6. Group discussion

Since the candidates will not be involved with later treatment of the survivors but concentrate only in providing Psychological First Aid, the above course details will provide an understanding of that subject only. The following course list will provide detailed theoretical contents as well as practical exercises during which candidates will be asked to deal with survivors in role-playing situations.

Psychological First Aid

Main skills required in crisis intervention:

1. **Befriending Skills**
2. **Listening Skills**
3. **Communication Skills**
4. **Practical Skills**

Because the staff have been selected to provide Psychological First Aid to other members of the work force, it will be of great benefit, especially in a large organisation, for the new carers to introduce themselves to their colleagues so that if a critical incident takes place, those affected will recognise the carers who will be giving support.

For those organisations who deal with customers or the general public, this should be dealt with during the initial training period.

Part two of this book will deal in detail with the main skills and behavioural aspects of the carer vis-à-vis the survivors.

Training should also be organised for both management and carers and plans made for procedures before an incident. Senior management should take charge of this detail. It may also be useful to appoint a supervisory carer to take overall control of the carer team.

PART TWO

The carer's essential skills

Befriending skills

First aid necessities

Listening skills

Communication skills

Practical skills

7

The Carer's Essential Skills

How do carers respond during traumatic exposure?

The following emotional, cognitive, behavioural and physiological reactions are often experienced by people during a traumatic event. It is important to recognise that these reactions do not necessarily represent an unhealthy or maladaptive response. Rather, they may be viewed as normal responses to an abnormal event. When these reactions are experienced in the future (i.e. weeks, months or even years after the event), or are joined by other symptoms (e.g. recurrent distressing dreams, 'flashbacks', avoidance behaviours and so on), and interfere with social, occupational or other important areas of functioning, a psychiatric disorder may be in evidence. These individuals should seek help with a mental health professional.

Emotional Responses during a traumatic event may include shock, in which the individual could present a highly anxious, active response or perhaps a seemingly stunned, emotionally numb response, or a described feeling as though the survivor is 'in a fog'. He or she may exhibit denial, in which there is an inability to acknowledge the impact of the situation or perhaps that the situation has occurred. He or she may develop dissociation, in which the person may seem dazed or apathetic and could express feelings of unreality. Other frequently observed acute emotional responses may include panic, fear, intense feelings of aloneness, hopelessness, emptiness, uncertainty, horror, terror, anger, hostility, irritability, depression, grief and feelings of guilt.

Cognitive Responses to traumatic exposure are often reflected in impaired concentration, confusion, disorientation, difficulty in making a decision, a short attention span, suggestibility, vulnerability, forgetfulness, self-blame, blaming others, lowered self-efficacy, thoughts of losing control, hypervigilance and perseverative thoughts of the traumatic event. For example, upon extrication of a survivor from a road traffic accident, he or she may cognitively still 'be in the vehicle', 'playing the tape of the accident over and over in his or her mind

Behavioural Responses in the face of a traumatic event may include withdrawal, non-communication, changes in speech patterns, regressive behaviour patterns, erratic movements, impulsivity, a reluctance to abandon property, seemingly aimless walking, pacing, an inability to sit still, an exaggerated startle response and antisocial behaviour..

Physiological Responses may include rapid heart beat, elevated blood pressure, difficulty breathing, shock symptoms, chest pains, cardiac palpitations (these symptoms, if present need immediate medical evaluation), muscle tension and pains, fatigue, flushed face, pale appearance, chills, cold clammy skin, increased sweating, thirst, dizziness, vertigo, hyperventilation, headaches, grinding teeth, twitches and gastro-intestinal upset.

What strategies can carers utilise to connect with particularly challenging individuals?

During traumatic exposure, individual reactions may present on a continuum from a totally detached, withdrawn reaction to the most intense displays of emotion (e.g. uncontrollable crying, screaming, panic, anger, fear, etc) These situations present a considerable challenge to the 'carer'. In order to address an individual's emergent psychological needs, you must 'break through' these emotional states.

1 Distraction

This technique aims to distract and refocus the challenging individual. The approach may be likened to a strategy that is often used by parents of young children. When the child shows interest in the TV remote control, the parent distracts the child with a 'transitional object' – a more appropriate, yet interesting toy. In the same way, when an individual is unresponsive to efforts to engage, or possibly at the other end of the continuum, is crying uncontrollably, you may distract and refocus the individual. Introduce an irrelevant yet highly interesting topic. The more concise and thought provoking the topic is, the better.

The key to this Distraction Technique is that the topic that is introduced, or the comment that is made is sufficiently powerful to distract or divert the individual's attention. Be careful not to say something that implies a lack of concern. Also, make sure that you subsequently return to the reality of the situation by discussing the event at a factual level.

2 Disruption

A second strategy that may be utilised with challenging individuals involves a powerful disruption of the emotional reaction. First, come down to the person's level, either kneeling or sitting and establish eye contact. In a clear calm voice, while looking directly into the individual's eyes, give a basic command using his or her name: *'Mary, I want you to take a deep breath.'* Continue to repeat the command, always using the same words. Escalate the volume and the tone with each command statement.

Usually, by the third command the individual will follow your request. At this moment, lower your voice to a calm level and begin to talk. You may instruct the individual to take a second and third deep breath. Once you have broken through the emotional state, you will be able to provide direction and support.

3 Diffusion

A third strategy for connection with the challenging individual involves diffusion of the emotional state. For example, you may begin your conversation with an anxious or possibly agitated individual at a voice rate and tone comparable to his or hers If the speaking voice is loud, increase your volume to match theirs. If it is rapid, again match the pace. If you are required to move around with the individual, match the speed. Gradually begin to slow the physical pace, lower the volume of your voice and slow your rate of speech. As the individual begins to respond in a calm, more controlled manner, provide direction and support. Move him or her away from the scene or stimulus, repeat the deep breathing and continue to encourage calmness.

Conversely, this technique may also be utilised in the opposite direction. For example, with a seemingly depressed or generally non-communicative individual, begin your conversation at a voice rate and tone comparable with that of the individual. If the speech volume is soft, decrease yours to match it. If you are required to move around with the individual, match the pace. Gradually begin to increase the physical pace, raise the volume of your voice and increase your rate of speech. As the individual begins to respond in a more energetic, involved manner, provide direction and support. Move away from the scene or stimulus, encourage deep breathing and continue to encourage calmness and help.

When considering the utilisation of Distraction, Disruption or Diffusion, be aware that time factors will influence your approach. For example, the latter diffusion technique, by its very nature will take more time to implement than either the distraction or disruption techniques.

These are practical intervention techniques. However, they must be practised. Breaking through powerful emotional reactions during a traumatic incident will require a confident, well rehearsed approach. Having a strong familiarity with these strategies will enable you to apply them with the most challenging individuals.

8

Befriending Skills

Psychological First Aid does not consist of counselling the survivor as soon as contact has been established. The individual, or group of people who have been involved in or witnessed a critical incident can develop psychological trauma. This is due to any abnormal, violent incident which goes beyond the coping mechanism of the survivor to whom it is happening and this can produce a shock to the system.

The affected person or groups of people will experience various reactions, depending on the severity of the incident. Some may be rooted to the spot, unable to decide in which direction to turn. Others will be unable to stop long enough to review the situation and aimlessly wander or even run in any direction.

A crisis occurs at the time or moment of severe trouble or danger. This can show plainly when an individual or group is involved in an incident where risk to the self is never far away or where they are not personally involved but are witness to the incident. This can produce severe fear for their own lives and that will produce a number of negative thoughts immediately after the incident, such as:

- What has or is happening to me?
- What will become of me?
- Is there any hope of rescue?
- What if I don't survive this situation?
- Am I safe?

This is the time when a qualified, empathetic carer should be at the scene of the incident to render Psychological First Aid in the form of practical support and assistance to the survivors who are very much in need of human contact at a time of severe crisis, reassuring the affected person or group that they are safe in the carer's hands

Approachability

It is a well known fact that whenever a critical incident occurs, where people are injured or have been bystanders at the scene of the incident, some 'do-gooders' will spring forward, in an effort do their good deed of the day and 'help' the traumatised individual. Their intentions may be very commendable but if knowledge of correct procedures is missing, then with the best will in the world, the bystander could do more harm than good and would be well advised to stand aside and let a qualified carer carry out the support.

The first task is to approach the survivor at a reasonable speed. Rushing up to them will only cause suspicion, nervousness and mistrust. Remember, they may have just had a severe shock and, to burden them with a barrage of questions at this early stage would be counter-productive.

If the survivor is sitting on the ground or on a chair produced by someone, do avoid towering over them which necessitates twisting their neck in order to look up at you. At this stage you will have no idea whether the survivor is in fact a casualty or is in shock and suffering from the after-effects of the scene they have just witnessed. Speak to them in a normal voice, shouting only makes them think you are more nervous than they are.

Introduce yourself by giving your first name and ask for theirs in return. However, don't be surprised if, due to shock they may have temporarily forgotten who they are. So, do not dwell on the fact that at this stage you don't know who they are. There could be someone near who will recognise the person and give you details of their identity. Should you suspect that the survivor is suffering from shock, first aid procedures will have to be administered which will be covered in the next chapter.

Reassurance at this stage will be very important and making it clear that you are there to help them and keep them safe from possible further harm should achieve a calming effect which, in turn will encourage the person to give you more information regarding their immediate needs. For example, there my be a need to look after small children, pick-ups from school or other duties which the survivor cannot carry out on his or her own at that time.

It may be necessary to move the survivor if the area they are resting in becomes unsafe. Unless the person has sustained injuries which prevent them from walking away from the scene, lead them gently to a more secure area, explaining in simple terms what you are doing and why it is necessary. You may have to ask a colleague to help you with this task but do keep the person informed in order to prevent a hysterical outburst.

Any practical issues requiring urgent attention will need to be carried out with the **least amount of fuss**, thereby avoiding further upset and anxiety for the already traumatised person.

Authority

Without appearing to be bossy and dictatorial, make it clear to survivors that you know exactly how to deal with their problems and are totally committed to helping them to overcome them. This does not mean that you will launch into a long explanation about the method you will employ to help them. The object of the exercise is to reassure the person that they should concentrate on getting over the shock of the incident and leave the practical issues to the carer. Your explanation about being a qualified carer will produce the required confidence in your ability to support the individual in the best and safest way.

If you need to involve other helpers or perhaps another carer, avoid leaving your survivor alone for any length of time. This will only encourage a return of the confusion they may have felt after the incident. Any request you need to make regarding their co-operation, should be done in a calm but and controlled manner so that there can be no possible argument which may waste time or bring about the return of adverse reactions.

If the carer works for a large organisation and has to deal with a major critical incident, it may help if some form of identification is worn, either a badge which must be visible to everyone or possibly an armband. This helps carers to carry out their jobs, particularly when there are people at the scene who should remain in the background. and can readily be asked to remove themselves so that the experts can deal with the situation.

Empathy

In order to make it easier and quicker to help someone who has been affected by a critical incident, you as the carer will have a very potent and powerful ingredient which will assist you in adopting a supportive climate – **empathy**.

This gives you the power, through your own personality to understand and communicate to the survivor your appreciation of his or her experience. By trying to understand the feelings which lie underneath the words or behaviour, you will be able to pass your understanding to the victim.

There is a great deal of difference between *empathy* and *sympathy*. If you become sympathetic, you will begin to feel sorry for the survivor which may encourage you to become part of the problem and produce considerable energy experiencing the other person's pain and suffering. Your support and caring mode will diminish and any decision making ability will decrease.

However, if you put empathy into practice your energy will be placed into understanding, communicating and acknowledging the other person's pain and suffering

You can develop your empathic skills by becoming more aware of the comments and information the survivor passes on to you. Active listening will provide you with many more details regarding the needs of the person, which include some of their feelings which lie underneath the hidden messages. This will provide you with positive proof that you have used empathic communication and that the survivor senses that you understand his or her predicament.

By making them aware that you are on the same level and fully understand their statements, for example: *'I can sense that you keep going over the same scene in your mind'* or *'you seem unable to concentrate properly at the moment',* will show the survivor that you are on their wave length.

Being a practical person

You as the carer will be required to be as practical as possible. By looking at the present situation and making a quick assessment of what needs to be done, then rolling up your sleeves and getting stuck in will do much to inspire confidence in the survivor. There are bound to be some disturbing sights around you and feelings of squeamishness have no place in such circumstances. Concentrate on the job in hand and make a mental note of the sequence of necessary tasks. For example, is the survivor in a safe place or will it be vital to move him or her further away from the disaster?

Make sure that while you are providing the caring support, at the same time look after your own needs so that you don't end up becoming a casualty yourself. Being comfortable with yourself in the knowledge that you are not struggling with unresolved traumas or recent bereavements, will enable you to provide a supportively effective Psychological First Aid service and have the ability to hand back control to the survivor once his or her traumatic shock reactions have been allowed to diminish.

9

First Aid Necessities

The employee/s who perform the task of crisis intervention, or Psychological First Aid, will only be involved with the injured and/or traumatised individual for a relatively short period and will basically work in an emergency capacity in order to help the survivor cope with the immediate aftermath.

Psychological First Aid is a one-off procedure which is offered to survivors immediately following an incident. At this stage, any traumatised person will be unable to look unemotionally at any logic or urgent requirements. The carer's job becomes that of a 'prop' for the traumatised person, giving support, performing any domestic or personal tasks or pass on any relevant information which may be essential immediately after the incident.

During crisis intervention, the carer rarely gives any psychological advice since the survivors are too overwhelmed by the incident to react to counselling and, at this stage, need personal space to measure their own coping mechanism. What the survivors look for is support, reassurance, an empathetic approach and relevant information to assist with their most pressing needs.

It could well be that the most pressing needs are in the nature of First Aid if shock signs and symptoms, as well as other possible life-threatening symptoms are apparent.

Signs of shock

1. The person's face will be very pale, often grey. The skin will feel

clammy or may sweat, often profusely, but will feel cold to the touch. This is an indication that all is not well since someone with clammy skin should feel hot, yet the skin feels cold. At the same time, anyone feeling hot would have a flushed appearance, but anyone in shock appears pale.

2, The person's breathing will be fairly rapid but shallow; this is often called 'puppy-dog yapping'. Because breathing is shallow, due to possible blood loss, less oxygen is inhaled. There may also be a gasping for breath, called 'air hunger'.

3. The third sign is a fast but thready pulse. When first taken it may be quite regular, but as time goes by, it may become more rapid, weak and irregular

Symptoms of shock

There are many symptoms that can be displayed by anyone in shock and trauma. Not everyone will have precisely the same ones and they will also depend on the severity and degree of the condition. The following main symptoms are often found.

- Since blood is pumped to the injured parts by redistribution, it will be withheld from other vital organs such as the brain, heart, stomach and so on. The person may feel nauseous, particularly if a heavy meal has recently been consumed. Vomiting may actually take place.

- A person in shock is often extremely thirsty, at times pathetically so, particularly if blood or fluid loss has occurred.

- Restlessness is another feature, where the person is unable to remain still for long. This could pose problems, particularly when a fracture has been sustained or the critical incident has been particularly severe and other survivors are equally badly affected.

● It would be inadvisable to put too much trust into information given by the survivor since confusion related to the incident my be experienced. If this is combined with restlessness, the person should not be left alone.

● Anxiety is another common symptom. Many things will prey on such people's minds, particularly if they have important meetings to attend, deadlines to honour or any number of other reasons.

● Nervousness and suspicion can feature in shock. The person could show mistrust and challenge anything being done to help. He or she may well become un-co-operative, argumentative or downright aggressive.

● Someone in shock may start to shiver and complain of feeling cold. This may be due to internal bleeding or heavy fluid loss such as vomiting.

Denial is sometimes found in someone who either refuses to believe or is unable to come to terms with the fact that 'something nasty' has just occurred. However long they deny the incident, eventually they do come to terms with their plight and admit that all is not well. Reassurance is most important in such situations, particularly taking charge of decisions on behalf of the survivor.

Treatment for shock

● **Concentrate on REASSURANCE to alleviate further anxiety.**

● **If the survivor's face is pale, raise the legs above the heart level.**

● **Keep the survivor warm by wrapping blankets round (over and under).**

- **Provided the survivor is not injured, a warm cup of sweet tea can be given – to be sipped at intervals.**

- **Where there is no improvement – this could be due to internal injuries – and the person gets worse, remove him or her to hospital.**

Psychosomatic shock

This type of shock could occur if someone suddenly witnesses a critical incident or is personally involved in one, but there was no physical injury. Shock can quickly develop, particularly if it causes intense worry which will increase the condition.

If you are called to help someone suffering from psychosomatic shock, without personal injury, a warm cup of sweet tea could be given but beware of allowing the person to drink it too quickly – be aware that they may be very thirsty. Encourage small sips slowly otherwise the person may start vomiting.

Your number one priority will be to provide plenty of reassurance. Never tower above the survivor but get down to their level, eye to eye. Hold his or her hand, which will provide you with the opportunity to monitor the pulse at the wrist with the forefinger and middle finger of your other hand. Talk quietly to them as raising your voice will only add to their anxiety. The majority of survivors will hardly be aware that their pulse is being measured since hand-holding gives them a certain amount of comfort.

Since there will undoubtedly be medical and/or para-medico assistance available after a critical incident, in the event of the survivor being injured in some major way, expert assistance will of course be available. However, the survivor may show signs of medical conditions which earlier were not evident. These may require more qualified assistance or even arranging for ambulance transport to hospital.

Angina

This is caused by 'furred-up' arteries which prevent a full supply of oxygenated blood reaching the heart muscles. In this instance the heart gets insufficient blood and must therefore work much harder to pump blood through the body. The person will have exerted much more energy and this will result in a cramp-like attack, forcing the person to stop whatever they are doing and rest. The attack, which is called angina pectoris will last from approximately half a minute to, at most, five minutes.

An angina attack will progress fairly fast and will reach its peak very quickly. The person will feel a severe, gripping chest pain which often travels up the left arm and into the jaw. You will observe a shortage of breath and the person will complain of a tingling sensation in the hand. There may also be a feeling of giddiness and weakness. At this stage you need not be misguided into thinking that you are witnessing a heart attack which will be much more severe, so there is no need to call an ambulance at once.

While the person is suffering from these reactions, they will be in no position to answer a lot of questions or be moved into other areas. However, you do need to ask four vital questions which will give you all the information you require and once you know the answers, you will know how to deal with the condition. These are as follows:

1. Have you had this before?
2. Do you know what this is?
3. Are you under medical treatment?
4. Do you take any tablets or other remedies such as aerosol spray?

If medication is required, you will be asked to hand these to the person but before administering them, ask when the last dose was taken and suggest that they see their doctor if too many are required to stem the attack.

In order to avoid fainting, do not place the survivor on a chair but place them on the floor and ask a colleague to kneel behind the person with knees touching their buttocks. Ask the person to draw up their knees to a 45-45-45 degree position, thereby preventing any strain.

Place yourself in front of the person so that you can monitor progress. As the attack lessens, you will hear them exhale which will indicate that the attack is nearly over. After a further rest, you will be able to carry out other important care for the survivor.

Heart attack

There is a possibility that, despite the fact that you have administered the prescribed medication, instead of the expected improvement, the person appears to be getting worse. This may be a warning that the person is suffering from a major heart attack which means that there is a blocking of vital blood supply to a muscle in the heart. With any luck it will not be a major one, but it will mean that the person will need to be taken to hospital and receive vital medical and nursing care.

By this time you will have realised that what you suspected to be angina has turned into a major heart attack and an ambulance should have been called. Make sure that symptoms have been explained to the ambulance personnel so that the call will become an emergency.

While waiting for the professionals to arrive, you can assist the person in the following way:

1. Put the person in the same 45-45-45-degree position as for angina
2. Some of the signs the person will present are:
   * ongoing vice-like crushing pain in the chest region which will persist
   * breathlessness and discomfort as in severe indigestion
   * profuse sweating, pale ashen face with cyanosed (blue) lips
   * pain down one or both arms
   * a weakening, rapid or abnormally slow pulse, which may be irregular
   * the person may become unconscious.

Above all, stay with the person and provide plenty of reassurance. Tell them frequently that an ambulance has been called and is on its way; be supportive without causing the person more stress.

Regular pulse monitoring will be necessary, results of which should be given to the ambulance personnel. In the event of the person getting into further difficulties, you may have to commence with resuscitation procedures at any time.

Asthma

Asthma is a condition caused by various allergies, particularly domestic dust, pollen, hey fever and dust mites. It may also be stimulated by certain medications. In some cases, an asthma attack may be brought on for psychosomatic reasons. Exercise can also contribute to an attack.

Our lungs are protected by a thin film of lubricating fluid which prevents grating when we breathe in and out. The lungs are composed of tubules and air sacks, reducing in widths as the base of the lungs is reached. Air enters through the windpipe into the bronchus, then passes into smaller vessels called bronchioles until it reaches minute, gossamer-thin air sacks called the alveoli.

Healthy lungs can inhale and exhale without any problems arising. The lungs of an asthma sufferer, once an attack commences, go into a spasm because of a narrowing of the bronchioles. The sufferer is able to take in air into the alveoli much more easily than expel it. The result is that more air remains in the lungs than can be shed and the person is constantly trying to breathe with fully inflated lungs. The neck and chest muscles will tense up as the person tries to use them to pull the upper part of the chest upwards and outward in order to maximise the capacity of the lungs.

An asthma attack can be extremely distressing and even cause panic, particularly if it is a prolonged one, if the person is unaware of a certain allergy or is experiencing a first-time attack. Medication will have been prescribed by the doctor which may be in the form of an inhaler, used to help dilate the air passages. Asthma sufferers generally know how to deal with an attack and usually carry a number of 'puffers' in pockets, handbags and any other place where they might be required such as drawers or cupboards.

It can happen that an inhaler at the onset of an attack is found to be empty or even missing. This will undoubtedly aggravate the event since the sufferer, who is already fighting to breathe out, now has no means of treatment – which will cause more panic. If not dealt with, this will become a vicious circle: the more the person panics, the tighter the chest muscles become, thus increasing the spasm further. The inability to expel all the air from the alveoli becomes more and more exhausting which, in turn, causes further distress.

Some of the signs that an asthma sufferer will present will include:

- there will be a very marked increase in breathlessness
- you may hear distinct wheezing on exhalation – if the attack becomes more severe the person will be unable to expel enough air to produce any wheezing sound
- the person will develop difficulty in speaking and may only be able to whisper
- there may be signs of blueness of the skin (cyanosis)
- the asthmatic will perspire
- the pulse rate will become rapid and strong
- the person will tend to breathe using the upper part of the chest muscles – you will recognise this as the shoulders will be raised and hunched on inhalation, with the body leaning forward.

In the absence of medically prescribed inhalers, various methods can be attempted to assist the person in reducing the spasm.

1. Loosen clothing, particularly round the neck.

2. Take the person to a source of air, such as an open window. However, a word of warning here: make sure that the attack was not brought on by an allergy found outside the window – for example, chemical spray on plants or pollen, etc. If the person is

known to you, this information should have been logged on your record cards. If not, you may be able to find out before the attack deteriorates.

3. There may be another person in your organisation also suffering from asthma and using the same medication as your survivor. If so, ask if you can borrow a few inhalations for your sufferer. A word of warning: never administer drugs or medication belonging to someone else to a sufferer 'in case it will help'. In the case of asthma, however, many people are prescribed precisely the same brand of inhaler so no harm will be done.

4. There are various positions that you can place the person in to ease laboured breathing.

    •   Sit them down with both arms resting along the edges of a table. Lean them slightly forward and, with reassurance, encourage them to concentrate on breathing out. This position allows them free movement of the upper chest and shoulders.
    •   Alternatively, stand them up facing a wall, bend both arms level with their forehead and lean their head against their hands. This should also bring relief.
    •   Talk to the sufferer quietly and reassuringly, at the same time place the flat of your hand on the upper part of the chest and, with circular movements, gently rub the chest. This provides a soothing and relaxing feeling and may help to dissipate the spasm.

If the attack is a severe one and does not respond well to inhaler treatment, the survivor should be sent to hospital. However, while waiting for the ambulance to arrive, the following procedure, recommended by the National Asthma Campaign, has been suggested:

    •   Provide yourself with a polystyrene cup and, instead of using the inhaler in the conventional way, i.e. breathing the vapour in through the mouth (where at best only half the required dosage reaches the bronchioles), make use of the cup as follows:

- Squirt the inhaler three to four times into the cup and ask the person to place the receptacle as near the mouth and nose as possible.
- Encourage the sufferer to breathe in as deeply as possible, which will cause the vapour to reach the affected parts more readily.
- Cut a hole in the bottom of the cup. The puffer can be squirted through the hole. Carbon dioxide builds up and assists respiration.

Pulse and breathing should be recorded at ten minute intervals and sent with the person to hospital.

Hyperventilation

This is a condition where a person over-breathes, caused mainly by psychological factors.. It may follow shock or severe anxiety which can produce an attack of hysteria or panic.

When a survivor hyperventilates, the increased ventilation causes more rapid gas exchange between the air and the bloodstream. This is fine; the body is quite happy to take more oxygen on board. However, during hyperventilation, more carbon dioxide is blown off into the lungs and the air. We do in fact need some carbon dioxide in our blood to maintain the correct acidity, but when we hyperventilate the carbon dioxide in our blood falls and the acidity changes. Nerves that are bathed in blood are sensitive to these changes. Consequently we start feeling light-headed and tingly, possibly accompanied by 'pins and needles' sensations. This is caused by an excessive loss of carbon dioxide due to extreme breathing. Nerves will start to discharge their electrical impulses and cause muscle cramps and spasms. To reverse this situation, more carbon dioxide is required and the following steps will help:

1. Depending on whether the attack is severe or mild and after assuring yourself that the person is not in any immediate danger, take them to a quiet place, speak to them reassuringly but firmly and leave them to compose themselves. The attack may subside without further intervention.

2. If the cramp-like spasms persist, place a large paper bag over the person's nose and mouth so that exhaled carbon dioxide is re-breathed. This will cause the spasms to reduce and stop hyperventilation.

3. You often find that after re-breathing carbon dioxide output, the person will not find it necessary to inhale for approximately one minute. Do not be alarmed by this as the individual will resume normal breathing.

These conditions are only a few of the reactions which survivors may experience after being involved in or witnessing a critical incident. It is very much advised that those who become carers for survivors, will undertake a full first aid course so that they are qualified to deal with any reactions which may befall the survivors. In the event of a number of casualties requiring rapid treatment, professional help will be on the scene to deal with serious injuries but will be available to give you assistance should this become necessary.

Stroke

Stroke is a condition affecting the brain. The blood supply may be interrupted by a clot or a ruptured artery. This could be due to high blood pressure or a disorder of the blood circulation. Which part of the brain is affected will determine the extent and site of the damage. In the case of a blockage affecting a major vessel, death will occur. However, many people with minor blockages survive and with competent physiotherapy regain movement of limbs, speech and other control.

The left side of the brain controls the right side of the body and vice versa, except for the head. It is preferable if a stroke happens on the right side of the brain as this does not affect the speech ability. How can this condition be identified?

- If the person presents a very sudden, violent headache, loses control of the bladder and/or bowels, becomes weak and collapses, it is very likely to be due to a ruptured vessel. Pain in the head can be excruciating and people have been known to tear out their hair. Unconsciousness may also occur.

- If a clot blocks the supply of blood, cells behind the blockage will die. Hopefully it will be a minor vessel so that others can take over blood flow by diversion. Brain cells, once dead, cannot replenish themselves as cells can in other parts of the body.

- The survivor may present loss of movement on one side of the body, possibly paralysis of the limbs. The mouth may dribble and, since there is loss of muscular control, the side of the face, including the mouth will drop.

- Speech may become slurred and could be confused with alcohol intoxication.

- The condition does not usually present pain or headache – in fact, minor strokes often go unnoticed at the onset.

How can you help? Naturally the survivor must be sent to hospital as quickly as possible.

- While waiting for transport, lay the person down on the floor with head and shoulders supported and slightly raised. Tilt the head on the affected side down and place a towel or other absorbent material under the chin in case of dribbling.

- Monitor the person frequently and undo any tight clothing.

- Should the person become unconscious, you may have to start cardio-pulmonary resuscitation.

- If breathing and pulse are present, place the person in the recovery position but remain vigilant until professional help arrives.

In the event of a major critical incident, ambulance, para-medical and medical support will be present on the scene very speedily and will deal with such situations. However, although these conditions do not arise often, carers are advised to become fully qualified First Aiders as well, which will allow them to recognise serious reactions experienced by survivors much more readily.

10

Listening Skills

> **THE PURPOSE OF GOOD LISTENING IS TO CREATE UNDERSTANDING IN THE MINDS OF OTHERS**

The second most important objective in the development of good listening skills is to enable you to build trust between you and the survivor. The person who you are about to take care of and support through a very emotional period needs to have confidence in your ability to listen and show empathy and how you indicate this through your responses.

Once survivors have gained the necessary confidence in your ability to take care of those needs and requirements which at that moment they cannot personally take care of, trust will quickly develop. By listening carefully to their 'stories' which will contain present feelings and fears, and by showing that you understand what is happening to them at that present moment, you will have achieved getting through the barrier which they may have built round themselves.

You will need to adopt an air of authority without becoming dictatorial which will enable people to lean on you and allow you to take some of their responsibilities off their shoulders.

Since the people who are suffering from immediate trauma will be able to sense your perceptiveness in gauging what needs to be done, they will hopefully allow you to take responsibility on their behalf and get things moving. However, this requires that your listening skills need to be finely tuned. There are a number of characteristics which are often skimmed over or even ignored when two people communicate with each other in their attempt to listen.

Being understood

Means getting something across to somebody else so that person knows exactly what you mean. This 'something' can be facts, or it can be your intentions, your feelings or your frame of mind

Being accepted

By getting survivors to agree with you, or at least give you a sympathetic hearing, they should be able to sense that your offer of support is genuine and thus accept your willingness to fulfil your part as a carer.

Getting something done

Getting people to act because they understand what you need them to do, why they should do it and sometimes how and when. Or by helping them to change their attitude towards something by showing it in a new light.

Understanding others

Learning how they feel about you, a particular situation, or conditions in general. It is important that you achieve this through successful listening – all communications are two-way, not just something that goes *from* you *to* others, but something that takes place *between* you and the others. Unless you practise it this way, you will be as handicapped as if you went about your job wearing ear-plugs.

Keeping eye contact

It is hoped that survivors are in a position to talk with you and give you some indication of the present situation and any other information relating to the critical incident and their involvement in it. It is essential that you turn your full attention to the words and keep eye contact with the person who is trying to give you information. Trying to listen to words as well as letting your eyes wander to things happening at the scene of the incident will do nothing to instil confidence and trust.

Your attention must be on the complete explanation which is being given to you. Paying attention right up to the end of the last sentence, instead of thinking about what you are going to say next, will give you the full picture instead of only part of it. Stay focused so that you get the complete picture about the survivor's ordeal.

Observation

Active listening skills include a number of the senses which are used when we attempt to make sense of the message the other person is trying to convey. The ear hears but the mind listens and, at the same time our eyes pick up body language which often passes out strong messages.

Tone of voice can often give away clues about the person's feelings behind the words which are passed on to the carer who can then check with the survivor. As was mentioned previously, listening requires the carer to pay attention and concentrate wholly on the needs of the survivor. If these skills are applied, it will show the survivor that you are fully focused on the problems presented by the affected person, and this will in turn instil trust and confidence in your ability to take over the support required at this moment.

Active listening also requires patience on the part of the carer. It must be remembered that the survivor has just been involved in or witnessed a critical incident and will be suffering from a number of adverse reactions. You may, in fact find that they are unable to relate facts or feelings in a cohesive way. This means that any information could be given in a confused or irrational way, therefore patience and empathy need to be applied. The fact that there may be more than one affected person to be listened to should in no way stop you from giving your whole attention to the survivor whom you approached in the first instance. In a major incident, there will undoubtedly be a number of carers available who will be able to take charge of just one survivor.

Interpretation

It is a well established fact that the words uttered by someone may have a hidden meaning underneath the words heard by a listener. For example, if the answer to a message is dealt with in too quick a manner, it could well be misinterpreted as, *'I am not going to be given the help I need right now, perhaps this carer is too busy'*, or if asked by the carer how the survivor feels at this moment, and the answer is *'OK'* , it could well be a silent request for, *'Don't bother me now, just leave me alone.'* You will have to use interpreting skills in order to decide how to deal with this situation as sometimes it is more successful if you hold the survivor's hand and reassure him or her that you will be with them to help in any way necessary and that it is okay to be silent.

Keep your attention focused on the survivor so that you do not miss any changes which may occur during the 'silent time'. If your attention wanders to other areas, you could miss vital clues or words which may be uttered very quietly.

Interpreting body language is also part of active listening and enables the carer to act on these interpretations.

Above all, make sure that survivors, if not too badly affected by the incident, are able to listen to you and understand what you are trying to do for them. Check with them frequently to confirm that you are getting through to them and they have heard you correctly and, if necessary, repeat the message, while looking straight at the individual and not over his or her shoulder at some distant object or scene.

11

Communication Skills

As was previously mentioned, all communications are two-way, not just something that goes from you to others, but something that takes place between you and others. In particular, when dealing with a survivor who has just witnessed or been involved in a critical incident, it is therefore most important to remember that, in order to communicate successfully, you need to make sure that both you and the other person are talking about the same thing. By being on 'speaking terms', you are simply exchanging ideas, facts and, above all feelings with your survivor so that he or she understands you as you mean to be understood – and vice-versa.

What you are, in fact, hoping to accomplish is to create understanding in the mind of those whom you are trying to support in an abnormal situation. What you will need to remember is that you live in a complicated world – a world of words that mean different things to different people, since their interests and background are different from your own.

So, how well you communicate will vitally affect how well you succeed. In this instance, since you are dealing with people who have just gone through a very emotional situation and are possibly unable to think in a rational manner, your approach and subsequent dealings with the survivors will largely depend on what kind of impression you create – whether you manage to penetrate their shock reactions and how clear you make the fact to them that you are here to help in any way they need support.

Since this is a one-off support procedure which will consist of three vital areas, the right communicative approach needs to be employed so that the person affected by traumatic reactions will feel 'taken care of' and you will achieve a reduction in anxiety, panic, fear, helplessness and a number of other characteristics.

1. Hopefully, if working for an organisation for whom you have been recruited as a carer in crisis situations, you will be known to anyone who is affected by the incident. However, when approaching the survivor, make sure that you introduce yourself by giving your first name and asking if you can be of assistance to the person. Never take for granted that you will be welcomed with open arms, since the individual's reaction to you may be less than responsive. Communicate calmly and don't overdo the empathy at this stage. Your first consideration must be to take the person away from any emotive scenes and make him or her comfortable.

2. Your second consideration must be to make sure that there are no injuries which the person is unaware of. In a major critical incident situation, the survivor may well have been hurt and, after the injury has taken place, adrenaline is released from the adrenal glands which are sited above each of the kidneys. Messages from the brain pass instructions that an increase of adrenaline be directed via the blood stream to specific parts of the body in order to protect or strengthen the injured part. Someone who has sustained a fracture often feels little or no pain since the adrenal response prepares the body for 'fright – flight – or fight'. For example, should it become necessary to flee from something threatening, a boost of adrenaline would be required by the legs. The survivor would not be aware of this until the adrenaline response wears off. Carers will need to be very vigilant and act promptly if there are serious conditions which they are unable to deal with. This will be the time to call for more experienced support.

3. As a carer, you will not be required to attempt to counsel the person suffering from traumatic stress response. You are there to

support the individual and help him or her to proceed through a process of coping and problem-solving abilities and encourage the person to re-gain control by going through a normal process during an abnormal event. Thus you will be taking quick action to change a presenting condition by adopting emphatic measures to move on.

Ability to champion a cause

Perception on the part of the carer goes a long way and often helps to speed up ways of providing fast intervention.

Effective communication skills are a necessary adjunct to the qualities required as a carer, particularly in situations where others may try to make decisions on behalf of the survivors which is not in their best interests. The carer must then intervene on the person's behalf and make certain that the reasons for the possible objections are really valid.

Ability to relate an accurate story

It may also be necessary to pass on accurate information to officials also involved in rescue operations and if the carer is less than articulate, it may show a confusing and inaccurate picture. A carer, well conversant with proper procedures, will be able to portray trust in his or her ability to see what needs to be done, will appreciate in what order of priority it requires attention and will apply common sense to create order out of chaos.

Ability to instil trust

Any practical issues requiring immediate attention need to be carried out with the least amount of fuss, thereby avoiding further upset and anxiety for the already traumatised person. The survivor needs to be fully aware that the carer is capable to carry out realistic requests without misunderstandings or even arguments. Should any requests be of an unreasonable nature, the carer should point out in an emphatic manner that there are more pressing needs to be carried out on the survivor's behalf and that the request can be dealt with at a later time.

Allowing the person to feel protected will instil trust and retain it.

12

Practical Skills

Common sense

Carers who have been assigned to give help and support at the scene of a critical incident should initially assess the situation. It is vital to determine if there are any circumstances which may endanger the safety of the carer or the survivor. There is little point in approaching the scene in a hurried manner if it ends up with further injuries or traumatic reactions before the carer has had the opportunity to make an initial check, since it is always necessary to take care of any possible injuries *before* dealing with psychological needs.

Individuals whom you have been assigned to deal with are very often not those who are immediate victims but those who have been witnesses, bystanders or even those who have had a second-hand description of the incident. Any one of these, having been exposed to these sights or descriptions, may well suffer from traumatic stress.

Depending where the survivor is situated, a quick visual assessment will tell the carer what the next move should be. If injury, however slight has taken place, then it may be necessary to obtain a more qualified person's assistance. If the survivor has actually moved away from the scene of the disaster and is wandering around, possibly still looking at the scene of the incident, the carer should make every effort to lead him or her to a less exposed place where the sight of horror is no longer visible.

Once the survivor is in a safe area and is able to communicate with the carer, it will now be the responsibility of this carer, having assessed the situation, to apply as much common sense as possible to deal with both the victim and his or her immediate needs. Their reactions may either be signs of withdrawal during which time the individual does not wish to acknowledge what has taken place. On the other hand he or she may become highly emotional which may include crying – even screaming, anger, fear or panic and so on. These reactions may necessitate breaking through completely, changing the subject and discussion. This may be one way of distracting and lessening the individual's emotional display.

The person may well need to tell his or her 'story' or a perspective of what has recently happened and should be permitted to talk about the incident and be allowed to voice his or her feelings about it. This 'shedding' will enable the distressed person to attempt to return to a more normal response and attitude.

It is the responsibility of the carer to engage in an educational, normalising phase as soon as it is possible which should assist the survivor to learn and understand how many people react to trauma. By pointing out that these reactions are normal in response to an abnormal incident should help the healing process.

Part of the common sense procedure is to assess the immediate needs of the survivor. This could relate to domestic necessities such as informing next of kin or perhaps for someone to pick up children from school or play groups. It is up to the carer to find out what these requirements are and arrange to have them taken care of on behalf of the survivor. The person may require transport to take them back to their homes or messages sent to friends or neighbours to help with the care of elderly relatives. The carer will have to make sure that the information given by the survivor is detailed and, above all correct. This may involve staff within the organisation such as personnel or human resources becoming involved.

Once all practicalities have been dealt with, it is advisable to remain with the person who might otherwise lose all the benefits and support already given. However, when more professional help arrives, the carer must be prepared to relinquish control and leave the next stage to other staff.

Seeing what needs to be done

Before newly appointed carers can take over the task of giving support to employees who have been involved in a critical incident, they will have to undergo training in a number of different areas. In the previous section, mention was made about the need to possess common sense in order to act as the 'prop' to survivors who have been affected adversely by the incident.

The training sessions will contain advice regarding the sequence of the carer's approach when dealing with those suffering traumatic stress reactions. Needless to say there will be no check lists available which advise the carer of the procedures to follow. This will depend largely on six questions the carer will require answers to so that they can feel prepared to deal with those suffering from traumatic reactions.

1. **What?**
2. **Where?**
3. **Why?**
4. **How?**
5. **When?**
6. **Who?**

When the call to attend a critical incident is broadcast, the carer will require as much information as possible so that no time is lost in getting to the area of the disaster. For example, what was the nature of the incident? Where is the incident located? Why did this happen and is there perhaps a danger that it might spread? How were the injured involved? When did the incident happen? Who was responsible and have the emergency services been alerted?

Needless to say, the answers to these questions need to be answered by a pre-arranged source and someone in a senior position should be made responsible for issuing this information to relevant staff.

As soon as the relevant information has been passed on and the required number of carers have made their way to the place of the incident, a mental plan of action can be evolved on the way to the scene. Once the carers have a visual idea of the number of affected individuals, their plan of action can be put into practice.

Naturally in the case of major incidents, a senior carer or supervisor should be responsible for the co-ordination of support. The following is an example of a possible sequence which can, of course be amended.

- It is possible that some people are so badly affected by what has happened that they may be wandering around aimlessly. You will need to gently lead them away from the scene, making sure that you take them into a safer area. Make sure you introduce yourself by giving your first name and tell the person that you are qualified and are there to help them.

- It would be very helpful to wear a badge with your name and the identification of 'Carer' clearly printed on it so that it is visible to anyone involved in the incident. This also helps to identify you and confirms that you are there in an official capacity.

- Be prepared that survivors may be severely affected by what has happened and may not react to your words. Therefore make an attempt to tell them that you intend to take them to a safer area.

- The individual may have been injured at the scene of the disaster but could be unaware of this. A quick examination will establish whether you can deal with the injury yourself or will require more experienced personnel to take over.

- It may well be evident that people are so shocked that they may not remember who they are. You will need to persevere with one or two simple questions to help establish initial information. Following this, anything which might throw some further light on the person's reaction will be more useful than to confuse the survivor more by a barrage of questions most of which will not register.

Any practical issues requiring immediate attention need to be carried out with **the least amount of fuss**, thereby avoiding further upset and anxiety for the already traumatised person.

● Once you have settled survivors in a safe area, make sure that they are comfortable and, above all, warm. Anyone suffering from shock may well be showing signs of shivering. If blankets are available, wrap the survivors up in them, particularly if they are lying down on the ground. Chill can cool the body down very fast.

● As soon as you have managed to get accepted by survivors and they are starting to communicate with you, try to get some relevant details about them, the situation and their present state. You may find that they will want to tell you about their experience and even describe their feelings resulting from the incident. Let them talk and check back with them if you don't understand some of the details.

● Do not try to describe any of your own reactions relating to similar experiences but keep the focus on the person whom you are trying to support. It would be counter-productive if distressed people have to deal with your stress reactions as well as their own.

● If you feel that it is appropriate to make physical contact with the person, such as holding his or her hand or putting your arm around the shoulders, do so but watch for body language and facial expressions in case the person begins to feel uncomfortable.

● As long as there are no signs of injury, the survivor may appreciate the offer of warm drink such as a weak cup of tea or decaffeinated coffee but stay away from any stimulants.

● Always report back about any requests which have been carried out on behalf of the survivor and confirm that they have been carried out. Any messages which have been left by relatives or friends and neighbours must be passed back to the survivor as soon as these arrive, in order to reassure the person that he or she is being supported.

- Your survivors may have lost articles belonging to them during the incident and this could be worrying for them. Get a good description of the articles and report the loss to the relevant department. Do not rely on your memory when you report any loss to personnel or other places but make a list in writing and read it back to the survivor before dealing with it.

- It is recommended that all carers receive a psychological debriefing after the critical incident in order to deal with any left-over adverse reactions from the incident. The management of the organisation should make this available approximately one week after the critical incident.

PART THREE

Caring for the Carer

Negative Reactions

13

Caring for the Carer

How can carers manage their own response to a traumatic incident?

Dealing with the psychological reactions and needs of people who have been involved, either as victims or bystanders, during a traumatic incident can be an exhausting experience. Providing care for individuals who are in severe emotional distress demands a great degree of energy which, for the carer, can often require both physical and mental input. It is therefore very important that you pay attention to your own well-being before you decide to provide support as a carer in Psychological First Aid.

If you are currently experiencing a time of emotional distress in your life, it would be more appropriate to allow another carer to provide support to the survivor. In this way you lessen your chance of becoming contaminated yourself by the critical event.

As a carer, you are likely to be exposed to the very events for which you are called upon to provide Psychological First Aid. For example, after arriving at a road traffic accident, police personnel will have the responsibility of dealing with the injured. While clearing the area of bystanders, they may also attempt to provide psychological support to anyone needing it. However, these officers may have also seen some very unpleasant and disturbing sights at the site of the accident. As a carer, you may also be exposed to very distressing physical incidents as well as the psychological impact that these events have on anyone who was involved, in whatever capacity.

There will be times when you will identify personally with a survivor with whom you are working – or perhaps with some aspect of the situation. For example, a group of Salvation Army officers attended an underground train disaster and were subjected to some very disturbing scenes of casualties who were being rescued by ambulance personnel and rescue workers. One army officer noticed a young child being carried out of the debris who looked very much like his daughter. At the end of his shift, he rapidly made his way home and his most important task then was to give his daughter a big hug after assuring himself that she was alive and well.

Despite drawing upon a specific strategy that will help you to remain 'professionally detached', powerful thoughts and feelings have a way of piercing professional detachment. **This is a normal response to an abnormal situation.**

- Maintain an awareness of your state of mind, as well as your physical reactions. Consider the effect the person is having on you. Acknowledge to yourself that your involvement with the individual is creating various physical and psychological reactions.

- If you find that the discussion is causing you to react physically (i.e. rapid heart rate, breathing increase, sweating, etc) take a slow deep breath and tell yourself to relax – take a second deep breath and relax. If possible, separate from the event, find a cup of decaffeinated coffee or tea and share your feelings with your peers.

- If you find that you are unable to concentrate, focus on the individual and the specific words they say – work to actively listen to what they are communicating. Slow down the conversation and try repeating what you have just heard.

- If you find yourself feeling emotionally overwhelmed, it is acceptable to acknowledge the impact the event is having on you as a human being. For example, you might say, '*what we are seeing here is really difficult for all of us ...'* However, make every effort to avoid self-disclosure of specific, personal information (e.g. *'this reminds me of when my sister was involved in a car accident ...'*). Remember that it is okay not to be okay and that displaying your emotions can reinforce for the survivor your genuine concern.

Finally, realise that traumatic stress may interfere with your ability to make good decisions and can therefore place you in danger. Monitoring your own reactions, while working with others during a traumatic event is critical.

If you find yourself feeling emotionally overwhelmed following the provision of Psychological First Aid, try the following:

● Acknowledge that the experience has been difficult for you.

● Realise that the connection that you established with the person can have a lasting impact on you. Words they have spoken and the emotions they displayed may become imprinted on your mind.

● Reflect upon what has just occurred. Be aware of your emotional, cognitive, behavioural and physiological reactions. If necessary, engage in some physical exercise to dissipate the stress energy that has been generated. Find a trusted friend to talk to about your experience. However, remember to keep in confidence things the survivor may have shared with you.. Talk about your reactions to the experience. Sharing the experience will help you assimilate what has occurred and to gain a sense of closure.

● If you find it difficult to sleep because of continual thoughts of the person's words or emotional display, realise that this is a normal reaction. Do not fight the sleep difficulty as this will usually pass in a few days. Try the following:
    a) Eliminate caffeine for four hours prior to bedtime,
    b) Create the best sleep environment
    c) You can consider taking a few moments before turning out

the light to write down your thoughts, thus emptying your mind.

d) Try reading or listening to peaceful music.

- Take some time to step away from the action. If possible, give yourself permission to rest, relax and engage in some non-threatening activity. Unwind.

- Spend time with your family and friends; stay connected with them. Resist the urge to retreat into your own world. You need their support following an emotionally charged event.

- If you have the opportunity, take advantage of a Critical Incident Stress Debriefing in the days following the traumatic experience.

- If necessary, seek the assistance of a professional. If you find that the experience is powerful and is staying with you for an extended period of time, allow yourself the advantage of professional support and education. Remember that you are a normal person who has experienced an abnormal incident.

- Have the strength to let go. It requires courage to face the powerful emotions within you.

14

Negative Reactions

There are many people who appear to have developed a very negative approach to providing help, support and any vital first aid which may even save a life. Even showing concern and empathy will often bring feelings of embarrassment which invariably stops the person from giving a survivor the necessary help which is so badly required at the scene of a critical incident.

Willingness to assist at these incident sites does not necessarily provide the person with sufficient courage to wade in and put personal feelings aside. There are many reasons why some people panic at scenes of disaster, yet some morbid fascination often compels people to rush towards the scene in order to 'just have a look' in case they can do something to assist. Deep down, these people know full well that their reactions will be negative and do more harm than good.

They may accept that their presence would not be in any way helpful, with perhaps the exception of calling for qualified help, if asked to do so. Once that is done, they are no longer providing any useful support and should remove themselves from the scene in order to give others a chance to provide qualified help.

There are many reasons why candidates for the post of carer should not even think of applying for the position.. The following characteristics and negative reasons will give some indication regarding the unsuitability of attempting to become a carer.

Fear of the unknown
Despite the best will in the world to make the effort to help those in need when disaster strikes, people often experience negative thoughts

regarding the responsibility attached to the task ahead. Adequate capabilities to deal with affected survivors are questioned and the possibility of further critical incidents happening stays in the back of the mind. People's own safety is questioned and reluctance develops to even attempt rescue operations.

This reluctance to join other helpers wastes very valuable time and can often do more harm to survivors who need support. Being honest with oneself and admitting that the job of caring for the afflicted is not one which would be successfully carried out, since fear of failure would be uppermost in that person's mind. It should therefore be left to those who are more qualified and stronger to deal with this type of disaster and the people who are affected by it.

Adverse first aid reactions

Many people feel that it would be helpful to attend a first aid course so that when a situation arises where help is required, they will be able to provide it. Dealing with minor injuries such as cut fingers, abrasions, strains and sprains and other easy to deal with injuries don't usually cause adverse reactions. The person who is attempting to deal with first aid requirements is not even aware that some more violent or serious injuries may well cause that person to produce more violent reactions.

The following examples should be examined and if these cause negative reactions, first aid attempts may have to be discarded since that person may well finish up being a casualty him or herself

- **Blood phobia** – as mentioned earlier in this chapter, small cuts do not usually produce heavy bleeding but, should the injury be of a more serious nature and the volume of blood escaping from the wound causing concern, this may well affect the would-be first aider much more seriously. It has been known that the sight of heavy bleeding may cause the helper to faint. This now means that there are two casualties which, in the event of a critical incident will only cause more problems for those who are now forced to leave what they are doing and help out.

    It pays great dividends to recognise the adverse reaction to heavy bleeding and prevent people from becoming casualties themselves. Leaving this kind of help to those who are able to deal with the situation without negative reactions will get the job done much quicker and more safely.

- **Allergy to vomiting** – It is possible that the survivor, due to reactions to the critical incident may have adverse reactions by having vomiting spasms which are often quite violent. Both the sight and smell could cause the helper to have a similar reaction by vomiting him or herself. This is likely to produce extreme feelings of guilt and inadequacy in the helper which, in turn could destroy the sense of trust the survivor has established with the carer.

  It is very likely that this kind of reaction will be known to the person trying to help, so it would be in their interest and that of the survivor to abstain from getting involved in the support of such events. Only helpers with a strong stomach control should take on such duties.

- **Embarrassment** – People who have experienced some form of shock often suffer from a weakness of the bladder or bowels and have involuntary reactions by passing urine or faeces. This will undoubtedly cause them further unwanted feelings of embarrassment and acute discomfort.

  These feelings can often be transferred to the person who is attempting to give support to the survivor which would interfere considerably in the carer being of help. Needless to say, the survivor will require attention to be cleaned up, made comfortable and to be reassured by the person looking after them.

  Embarrassment has no part to play in such a situation and if any of these resulting characteristics exist on the part of the carer, it would be kinder to refrain from performing any personal tasks. There are many duties which people can provide which do not produce unexpected deep seated feelings which will cause further stress.

- **Lack of Empathy** – There is a great deal of difference between showing empathy to someone who has been involved in a traumatic incident and displaying sympathy related to the experience. The survivor will either have been removed from the incident site or may still be in situ while the event continues to develop around them. During this time, individuals may be at their most vulnerable and will be stimulated by thoughts and feelings related to this or past incidents. Survivors who are exposed to critical incidents and trauma will require maximum support at this time and the absence of an emphatic approach will hinder any improvement in their condition.

At this time an empathetic approach toward those who are supported by a carer will achieve realisation, understanding and the opportunity to communicate an appreciation of the survivor's experience. The empathic approach allows the carer to understand feelings which lie underneath words or actions, thereby enable this understanding to be conveyed to the survivor.

It is, however, unfortunate that in reality many people who attempt to give this vital support to the afflicted, tend to look the other way. Some individuals are inclined to feel extremely unprepared to deal with those who are experiencing painful thoughts and feelings and tend to feel uncomfortable or afraid that the wrong responses may make matters worse.

In these circumstances someone who takes on the duty of an emergency responder may confuse empathy with sympathy which will only serve to make the helper feel sorry for the survivor. Being sympathetic may encourage the helper to become part of the problem, thus becoming 'victimised' as well. This will cause an investment of considerably more energy being spent on the survivor's suffering and the ability to remain functional and retain decision-making abilities will undoubtedly diminish.

A sympathetic approach does not belong to critical incident situations and those who fail to recognise the difference or are unable to develop an empathic manner should refrain from becoming a carer.

- **Unresolved trauma** – Most people have at some stage in their lives experienced or been involved in a traumatic incident. Depending on the coping mechanism in their make-up, reactions to this do not overwhelm them and, after a few days where thoughts of the incident intrude, people manage to come to terms with the memories and 'get on with their lives'. However, others will keep the incident at the forefront of their minds and fail to remove the event out of their memories.

  Unless the person takes steps to consult someone who can help the individual to make sense of their experiences so that they can move on, their traumatic experience may well lay dormant for lengthy periods.

  It is often thought that those who have been through a traumatic incidents will make good carers since they can understand what the newly traumatised person is going through. However, unless the carer's unresolved trauma has been dealt with, the carer may proceed to identify with the survivor and return to their original traumatic reactions. This can create a harmful situation and will only be resolved if the carer seeks help him or herself before continuing with the task of providing care. The person should have the strength to withdraw support and find someone else more suitably equipped to take over. .

- **Lack of communication skills** – One of the most important characteristics in providing care to those who are affected by traumatic stress is to possess good communication skills and the one which stands out more than any other is to be a good listener.

  Unfortunately many people are unable to spend the necessary time listening but invariably cut into the words their communicator is trying to convey. This can do quite a lot of damage to someone who is already confused and stressed, since they realise that the carer is not really listening to their 'story' but assumes that they know the end of the tale. Assumption can produce quite a lot of further stress and trust may also be lost.

  People who use these tactics in order to move quickly onto the next part of the communication will spoil any attempt to create understanding and should practise more self control in order to improve their listening skills. Assumption will always create misunderstandings and will certainly not achieve the important task of turning panic into calm.

What constitutes an unsuitable carer

The majority of people will be very willing to lend a hand and help as best they can when incidents occur where casualties and those affected by abnormal sights require someone to take care of them.

Not everyone who comes forward to help is either trained in caring or capable to do it at all. The above reasons for the unsuitability of individuals are by no means the only ones and it pays good dividends to look closely into your own make-up in order to make quite sure that you will be suitable to carry out a carer's duties.

Above all you need to be very honest with yourself. There is little point in believing that you will 'get used to the sight of blood' or remain calm and focused when dealing with people who are relying on you to give them support, or minor first aid or take care of some of the practical issues which the survivor may not be capable of dealing with at that time.

You may become aware that common sense is not very high on your list of priorities and consequently your understanding of such a situation will take time, which in a critical incident is something you don't have. On the other side of the coin there is little to be gained in rushing around, causing interruptions to others who are attempting to provide support.

Un-decisive behaviour when fast decisions and actions are required will only cause others to lose valuable time in helping those who are in trouble. If you are a slow thinker or are the kind of person who requires time to come to a decision, your place in a disaster area is not in the centre of it since often, quick decisions have to be taken in order to avoid further disaster, chaos and confusion.

Too much in control

Some people need to be in control of every aspect of their lives and the numerous activities which they fill their lives with. Any situation which arises will instantly encourage them to take the task over. In other words 'take control' is uppermost in the minds of such individuals.

This type of behaviour will undoubtedly cause stress since the attitude of being able to cope with anything which comes along will eventually create a breaking point. These super-human attempts have a habit of creeping up when you least expect it and thoughts like: 'I can cope' and 'I have enough energy to see it all through on my own' or, 'I don't need help from anyone' will produce negative results and stressful reactions.

This type of person will certainly not be a suitable person to take care of and support survivors from a critical incident since, underneath all this energy and control-taking lives someone who has a n enormous 'be strong' attitude which prevents them from showing human attributes such as emotions.

'Big boys don't cry' and 'coping' are major attitudes in the lives of these individuals and tears are not part of those – neither are feelings. The need to appear strong is always uppermost in their minds and, before they can even contemplate becoming a carer, they need to recognise that it is okay not to be okay and develop the ability to let go.

PART FOUR

The Voluntary Carer

Coping with Personal Crisis

The Survival Pack

Support Team Work

Conclusion

15

The Voluntary Carer

Apart from industrial and commercial incidents which will be dealt with by the emergency services and an appointed number of carers which are part of the employees, there are a multitude of critical incidents, such as RTAs (road traffic accidents), assaults, burglaries or robberies, especially in busy shopping areas, which will affect the general public who either witnessed this or were personally involved.

Unfortunately these situations often create panic or chaos and willing but untrained carers will attempt to do their best to get stuck in and help those in need. The victims of the incident often requires first aid and, although emergency support has been alerted, there is no guarantee that they will arrive at the scene in record time. And if all this happens in either morning or evening rush hours, there is likely to be even more panic.

It is most commendable when well-meaning road users, pedestrians and home owners come forward to try and help in any way they can but, with the best will in the world, untrained individuals will unfortunately only help to cause more confusion by getting in the way of those who are more qualified to deal with the incident and its survivors.

The main body of this book concerns itself with the recruitment, selection and training of carers and the support which they would carry out in the event of a critical incident taking place in a work environment. In this situation, careful investigation for suitability of successful applicants will have taken place and necessary training provided before candidates will have sufficient knowledge and understanding required to undertake caring for critical incident survivors. There will be management to support and advise the appointed staff by providing back-up in case of need.

The self-appointed carer is a different animal and will come forward from choice and will have to cope with the necessary support through realistic assessment of the situation, what back-up will be needed and numerous other vital requirements which he or she will have to take responsibility for.

In case of additional help which may from time to time be required, it may be possible to request assistance from the usual bystanders who gather at these scenes. The main thing to emphasise at the outset is that, since the self-appointed carer has taken on the responsibility of dealing with survivors, he or she needs to make it clear that he or she is in charge of the particular case with which help is required. For example, this may include moving the person further away from the incident to a safer place.

The emergency services will hopefully be in situ by this time and it is always a sensible idea for the carer to make him or herself known to them in case more professional help is required. This will also give the carer back-up with untrained people willing to help.

If 'carer' training has taken place, evidence of this should be available, ready to be shown to people in charge at the site of a critical incident and, hopefully proof of the qualifications, in the form of a badge or armband will be provided so that authority to deal with affected survivors will be visible.

After an assessment regarding the number of survivors requiring assistance and support, and a rough estimate of the seriousness of the incident have been made, requests for emergency services must be sent and, in the case of a road traffic accident having taken place, someone should be delegated to close off road entrances so that no further accidents can take place.

Method of procedure

- As a carer you should be in possession of a first aid certificate, either that of an 'Appointed Person' which will have instructed you in the emergency procedures of first aid or, preferably a full HSE approved course giving you the official certificate lasting three years. You will have to take a further course to re-qualify at the end of the three year period.

- Always make it known to the person to whom you are giving support that you are a Qualified First Aider as well as a carer. Introduce your self by your first name and ask if you can help in any way. Never assume that you can just wade in and assume that it will be accepted by the survivor. You must never forget that this person has just been involved in or has witnessed a critical incident and will have received a shock to the system. Traumatic stress may well follow which means that he or she will be incapable of thinking straight and may even be unable to understand any questions you put to them.

- Despite the fact that you may find it difficult to communicate with them at this stage, make sure that you explain to them in simple terms what you intend to do to make them more comfortable and sort out any important issues on their behalf, if possible.

- Remember that your job as a carer does not require you to attempt any counselling since at this stage the survivor will not be able to react in a positive manner to this. Your task is to allow the person to overcome the shock they may be suffering from and, if possible, to receive help from you with some of the material issues which they are not capable of carrying out themselves at this point in time.

- If you find that relatives or friends need to be informed by telephone, do not hare off and leave the person unattended while you deal with a request. It is much better to engage the assistance of someone else who can be trusted, but make sure that this person reports back so that you can put the survivor's mind at ease.

- Always communicate with your survivor at the same level; if they are sitting down or even lying down, do not tower above them as this will add to their anxiety. Your tone of voice should not be too loud as this may indicate that you are as nervous as they might be which will be anti-productive and lose you valuable trust.

- You may feel that the person whom you are supporting will benefit from some physical comfort such as putting your arm around their shoulders or holding their hand. Watch for signs of rejection and resist the temptation. It is always necessary to take a pulse reading if someone is suffering from the after-effects of shock. Ask the person if they will allow you to do this. Hold their right hand with your right hand, which will comfort them and then, with your left hand place your middle and forefinger on their inside wrist and take a reading for one minute. A normal pulse reading is usually between 65 – 80 beats a minute but in the case of shock or the after effects of traumatic stress, this will vary. If you are in doubt, refer to the emergency services or paramedics. (a description for the treatment of shock can be found in an earlier chapter).

- Once survivors have settled down and are capable of communicating with you, they may find it helpful or even necessary to tell their story. This will mean that you will be required to listen, making it clear from time to time that they have your undivided attention. However, this is not the time to go into a discussion about the incident or to give your own views, feelings or reactions, but to allow survivors to return to a feeling of normality. Show empathy, not sympathy as this will undo all the good work you have so far achieved.

- It is essential that, although you have taken control of the needs of the survivors during a period when they could not cope with the situation, you eventually give back this control to them. They need to understand that although the incident was an abnormal one, their reactions were normal.

● It will also be helpful if you make survivors aware of possible reactions which may show themselves at a later date, possibly days after the experience. This is where a debriefing of the incident will be beneficial and a visit to their GP is advised so that this could be set in motion.

● As soon as survivors are relatively calm and can give you personal details, make notes of the date, time and incident as well as names, addresses and other useful information in case these are required at a later date. Never leave people to fend for themselves too soon after a critical incident, but make sure they are in competent hands. Depending on the outcome of the exercise, you might like to check by telephone later just to reassure yourself that your support allowed the individuals to overcome the stressful reactions.

16

Coping with Personal Crisis

At some time or other, everyone goes through a crisis, critical incident or tragedy. People have accidents at home – young and old can die unexpectedly. You or someone in your family may become very ill or you may witness a critical incident away from your home.

A tragedy is nearly always something we feel could have been avoided. It is something we are unprepared to meet, something that leaves us with all sorts of confusing and unpleasant feelings.

For many, the worst time is when all the fuss has died down but the strong feelings remain. Everyone expects us to be alright – and we are not. The world goes on much the same as before while inside we may feel alone and that no-one understands.

You may think that you ought to be coping better, that you are not dealing with things as well as others might. This may mean that you don't tell those around you how bad things really are, because you are ashamed about needing or asking for help.

The following chapter will help you to understand your reactions, to know what to expect and to know what to do.

Reactions in the early weeks and months

Shock

Initially, you may feel very little or nothing at all. You may have difficulty taking in what has happened. Everything may seem unreal. Some people describe being 'in a dream', or as if things were happening to someone else.

Thoughts about what happened

Painful pictures of what happened may push their way into your mind. You may find yourself going over things again and again, or re-living the feelings you had at the time.

Anger

Strong feelings of anger are common. The event may seem so senseless and you may feel picked on – 'why me?' You may feel badly treated by 'the authorities' You may want to blame someone. Your anger may be expressed at everything and everyone..

Fear

When things go badly wrong, we become aware how easily such things can happen, and how unsafe we really are. The world around us can now seem much more dangerous.

You may feel frightened that the same thing could happen again and fear for the safety of those you love. You may grow over-protective towards your children or scared to leave your own home.

Shame and guilt

No matter what actually happened or what you did, it is often the case that people feel guilty. You may wonder if you should have done more for others or why you should be alive when others are not.

Helplessness

You may feel totally out of control of your feelings and of what happened to you. You may feel ashamed about this or anxious about the state of your mind.

Loss

If you have been bereaved, the sense of loss may feel overwhelming. Some describe waves of physical sensations which can come and go at any time. Deep feelings of sadness, anguish, grief and hopelessness may follow.

Your body can be affected

Some feelings are experienced in your body. This may cause you to worry that you are physically ill when, in fact, your body is showing signs of your emotional distress. The following are common:

- tiredness
- a racing heart and the shakes
- feelings of sickness and diarrhoea
- difficulty in breathing
- tightness in your throat and chest
- headaches
- neck and backache.

Sleep problems are common too:

- it is hard to get to sleep
- you may wake in the middle of the night
- you find yourself waking very early.

Loss of interest

You may discover that you are not as involved as you were in your usual everyday activities. You may not even notice this until someone tells you. You may feel numb and you may be unable to experience the feelings that you used to have.

Loss of confidence

You may also have a loss of confidence, in that you worry about doing everyday jobs. What you once took in your stride, now may seem very difficult.

● Feeling cut off

You may feel cut off or distant from people you love and are normally close to. This, with the irritability and anger you may have, can make relationships very difficult.

It is very important to know that these feelings are normal and understandable reactions to abnormal events. Although they are very intense and difficult to put up with, these are the way ordinary people can feel.

What are the most useful things to do?

- Don't expect memories and feelings to go away quickly – they will come and go for a while.

- Trying to forget, or avoiding things to do with the events may seem a good idea at the time. Trying to push things to the back of your mind can be helpful for a short while. But it may be impossible to forget – the thoughts may return however hard you try. You won't forget things, but you need to reach a point where remembering is not so painful.

- Getting better comes from allowing feelings to come out. Showing anger and sadness can be helpful. Keeping feelings in will be a drain on your energy.

- Try to share what has happened to you with people who are prepared to listen. It is a mistake to think that 'no one understands'. This may be embarrassing at first, but talking does help. However, don't get involved with too many people – find one person to talk to over time.

- Don't forget that children need to talk as much as adults. Let them show their feelings in games and drawings. Do let them get back to school, but discuss with their teachers what has happened. School friends may be cruel to them.

- Other people who share the same sort of experience can be a great help to you. Take the opportunity to meet with them.

● Take good care not to drink or smoke too much. It may only help for a short while and then become a problem itself. The same may be true of sleeping tablets or tranquilisers.

● Do drive more carefully and take care at home as accidents there are more common after stress.

When should you ask for help?

You can ask for help anytime, but especially:

● if your feelings have not begun to fall into place after a couple of months and you are still feeling tense, confused, exhausted, uncontrollably angry, anxious, or very low
● if you continue to feel numb, or are keeping active so as to shut out your feelings
● if you continue to have poor sleep or nightmares
● if you have no-one to talk to and you feel the need to do so
● if your relationships or work is suffering
● if you think you are smoking or drinking too much or taking too many tablets

There is no shame in asking for help. It does not mean you are weak or useless. The help of an outsider is not an easy answer, but may help you get things in order in your mind and use your strength to better advantage.

It must be understood that anyone who trains and takes over the duties of a carer is not a trained and qualified counsellor. Therefore if some of the above mentioned symptoms are becoming obvious during your care and listening skills, it is important to suggest that your survivor attends either a de-briefing session which should be organised by your company or, if you have undertaken to provide Psychological First Aid outside the work place, that the person makes contact with a qualified counsellor who will be able to deal with the symptoms.

Your skills as a trained carer will be extremely important immediately after a critical incident and will give the necessary support to anyone suffering from traumatic stress.

17

The Survival Pack

Identification badge or armband

It is vital that in any critical incident, those who come forward as trained and qualified carers, should wear some form of identification to let others know that they have a right to be there and assist wherever necessary.

Ideally this identification should include a recent photograph of the carer on the identi-badge and this must be encased by a plastic cover to protect it from damage. In the case of employees recruited to perform this task, the name of the organisation further identifies the carer. Those who come forward in outside incidents may get such an identification card from the organisation who provides training, in which case that company's details will be on the certificate which the carer will be required to sign.

Nurses who have received first aid training will have their own identification.

First Aid kit

It is advisable that every car driver should provide him or herself with an adequate First Aid box, housed in the boot of the car. As soon as material from this box is used in any emergency, the items supplied to a casualty should be replaced and, in any case the contents of the box should be inspected frequently to make sure that the box is fully operational when required.

Replacement supplies can be obtained from any large chemist stocking such aids. No First Aid box may contain medications of any sort and if this is requested during an incident by the survivor, the carer must inform the person that they are not qualified to administer medication.

Only medication which has been prescribed by a medical practitioner and is in the casualty's possession can be given at his or her request. For example, tablets or spray in the case of angina or any other diagnosed condition which has been confirmed by the survivor.

Blanket

A warm blanket will also serve a useful purpose, particularly if the survivor is suffering from shock and will need to be kept warm.

In the case of the carer being employed, items should be kept in an accessible place, together with means of transportation of these emergency materials to the incident site. Naturally, for organisations employing carers, the items mentioned should be available in multiples.

Warm clothing (as required)

A critical incident can happen anywhere, at any time. Survivors are usually transported as soon as possible to places away from the disaster area, which may mean that they could be exposed to the elements for lengthy periods.

The emergency services, once they arrive at the scene, will have suitable apparel on board and storage of such necessities can be made available in organisations. Should an incident occurs in a public place or even in a residential area, such articles might be borrowed or even held in the back of the car to be used in case of need. For example, a warm jacket or coat, rolled up to preserve space. Alternatively, plastic blankets will protect people from the cold and should always be available.

If the survivor needs to be taken to hospital by ambulance, the goods belonging to the carer must be returned before the ambulance departs.

Protective clothing in adverse weather conditions

Rainwear is another essential necessity. In the absence of such apparel, plastic sheets, which can be folded and stored easily will aid survivors and protect them from getting soaked. Naturally, every effort should be made to move anyone exposed to adverse weather conditions.

An umbrella is also a necessary gadget to have in the car or store-room of the organisation. The most useful of these is a golfing umbrella which has a very large dome and can protect more than one person, if necessary.

Torch and spare batteries

There is little point in storing a little pocket torch unless it is being used in order to examine eye problems and this needs experience in first aid procedures. Critical incidents can happen at any time of the day or night and it is essential to have a reasonably suitable, large enough flash light which gives out a good beam.

Since this may have to be used for longer periods if night caring is required, a stock of batteries must be kept in reserve so that continuity of light is available. It might even pay dividends if the flashlight is duplicated in case help from another person is required.

If that is the case then a larger supply of batteries should be available. This, of course will assist if there is a mains power cut, perhaps due to the incident itself, and it is at this time that adequate light is available.

Bottled water

There are many reasons why water should always be available if a critical incident has taken place and, if working in an organisation and supplying carer support, water must always be stored and available.

This may need to be used for cleaning wounds, providing sips or sponging lips in case of shock where thirst is one of the reactions or keeping the fluid level topped up. The carer him or herself may be in need of a drink, or for any other hygienic purposes.

It is advisable to check the date when the water becomes unusable and replace the contents with another bottle (or more) If in the field, a supply of 'Still, Natural Mineral Water' should be kept in the car and changed when out of date. It is very easy to become dehydrated through lack of water and people should be very aware of this condition, especially during a major critical incident where there may be many survivors left without water.

Paper tissues

Boxes or packets of tissues can be used for many purposes and therefore a good supply should always be kept in store or in the car. Although some of these tissues are very small in size, they are better than nothing but, preferably man-sized tissues serve a better purpose.

Once used, a plastic bag should always be in situ so that dirty tissues can be safely kept away from survivors and disposed of at a later stage. There should, of course be a supply of medi-wipes in the first aid kit which are more serviceable since they do not disintegrate as much as paper tissues.

Surgical gloves

Any first aid kit these days should include a packet of surgical gloves. If open wounds need to be treated and the carer has an open wound anywhere on their person where it is likely to come into contact with the blood of the survivor, it is essential that they protect themselves by slipping on the gloves before commencing the cleaning-up process.

Once the job is finished, these used gloves should be discarded, ideally by burning. In critical incident situations, this may not be possible at the time, therefore the gloves should be placed into plastic bags and removed as soon as possible.

Pad and pencil

The carer may be required to carry out, or pass onto someone else a duty which survivors cannot carry out due to their condition. This might be the care of elderly relatives, picking up children from school or nursery or any other regular obligations.

This service may involve information which is better written down in detail, since it may have to be passed on to someone else who can deal with it.

Other information can also be noted down, such as medical details which need to be passed on to emergency teams who will need to inform staff at the hospital if the survivor is to be taken there.

This written information will require the carer's name, address and any other relevant details so that they can be contacted if necessary. The carer's signature will also be needed.

Carers in employment

The organisation which employs carers who take over the role of support staff, providing Psychological First Aid during a critical incident will be required to fill in official information sheets containing details of the people whose care they took over and the results of this support.

Copies of these sheets should be readily available immediately after the survivor has been transported to other sources, either hospital or other means of trauma treatment.

The carer should always print the information or, if available on the computer network, should fill in details at the earliest possible opportunity so that no details are lost or forgotten.

This is by no means the full extent of the survival packs which need to be available if a critical incident occurs. The range will depend largely on the type and seriousness of the incident and how many carers will be required at the time.

In any outside event, it will also depend on how many trained carers are willing to come forward to provide the essential Psychological First Aid support.

18
Support Team Work

Support skills

A major crisis, or a series of lesser crises, can stretch the normal capacity to cope with problems to its limit and beyond. For a time, people in crisis may become helpless and need others to step in with support. Anyone who understands what is happening and knows what to do is of great value in such emergencies.

The death of someone close is the most common cause of temporary 'crisis' breakdown. If a traumatic accident coincides with bereavement, the stress is additionally hard to bear. There may be uncontrolled weeping, or angry shouting, apathetic helplessness or restless activity. Often relatives themselves are stunned and at a loss to know what to do.

The support team worker or carer needs to have in mind a strategy which will help to reduce the chaos to manageable scale while at the same time bringing comfort when people face irreversible loss.

A strategy for handling crisis

1. **Quietly take command** Introduce yourself
   Check name of person(s) you are supporting
   Speak slowly and calmly
   Be a steadying presence
   Give information several times and in writing if necessary

2. Allow feelings to be expressed respond verbally, using brief sentences consider whether touch is appropriate allow tears – accept the reality of their experience

3. Clarify the situation Identify losses and immediate needs – accommodation, food, telephone calls to family, transport, clothing. Information.

4. Mobilise resources Specialist needs – medical, interpreter, religious family/friends/colleagues network – their support resources. Personal inner resources.

5. Action Explain necessary procedures – police interview, rest centre. Help them decide what their next step will be – go home or to relatives/ friends, accept accommodation if relatives hospitalised, how further help will be made available.
Explain any available leaflets (Personal Crisis)

Note: At the early impact phase of an emergency experience, practical help is one of the best ways of giving comfort, but not to the exclusion of the above strategy outline.

Support workers (carers) form an important stage in the helping process. It is essential not to force on people help they do not need, but most will appreciate the personal interest and practical assistance offered.

Most survivors and relatives say: '*I can't remember what you said but I'm so grateful you were there*'. The quality of immediate support given will influence whether they will ask for further help if needed after several weeks when symptoms have not begun to subside. A good experience of support will also make the task of specialist carers easier so the support worker is a vital first link in the chain.

In order to follow out the strategy, certain skills are required. Each worker will follow in his or her own personal style but the skills below are adaptable to anyone's own way of giving comfort and enhancing the capacity to respond.

Comfort Skills

1. **Introduce yourself** in a clear friendly manner and get the names(s) of those being supported.

2. **Contacting Skills**   A warm and accepting presence – but not over the top in sympathy. Eye contact frequent – don't gaze around as if not really interested. Voice should be firm, not too quiet for ambient noise level, even-volumed. Consider carefully touch – from holding of very distressed person to a light pressure on the fore-arm.

3. **Listening**   This is the only way to know what is appropriate to say. During their narrative, just an 'Mmm' says: I'm listening, do go on.

4. **Reflecting Skills**   Being able to say in your own words back to them what they have just said – or rather the gist and heart of what you have picked up. By doing this, you show your understanding which is experienced as very supportive.

5. **Reassuring**   Your calm presence is the best reassurance you have to offer. If you go away before they have finished, you convey that what they are describing is too painful for you to bear – which feels very rejecting.

   The anxiety of support workers shows when they over-reassure. There are aspects of a terrible experience which will never be put to rights and you lose credibility if you are superficial. You can assure the injured that medical help is on its way. You can say something like: *'This is a terrible experience and, just now everything seems pointless, but there will be special help for you – and you will come through it'*. Other predictions are not wise or helpful.

6. Relaxation

Techniques to steady someone who is very anxious starts with help to steady breathing by slowing it to a less panic-stricken rate. Finding where the muscles are being held in tension and relaxing them can be calming.

Baths and walking can also refresh and relax.

7. Centring

Imagine a centre within yourself, linked to but distinct from your thoughts and feelings. Here is a point of peaceful well-being you can associate with a favourite holiday scene and focus upon while doing the breathing exercises. These items may not be possible in the activity of a reception area but can be introduced when accommodated at rest centres or hotels.

8. Family Network

This remains one of the best resources for comfort and people can often be calmed by the thought of imminent reunion with family members or close friends.

19

Conclusion

Industrial and commercial outlets are dependent on regular and effective output of products as well as a workforce which is properly trained, has all the necessary tools available and benefits from a safe working environment.

Although the majority of managers make sure that the company works on oiled wheels by providing supervision and staff who can deal with employee problems when they occur, it is often difficult to identify the cause when a member (or members) of the work force shows signs of slowing down, unusual behaviour not normally found and even reporting sick more frequently than usual.

In some cases it is very difficult to identify the presence of post traumatic stress reactions, particularly if an incident has happened outside the workplace. Management often believe that they are not responsible for anything which occurs outside the gates of the workplace. What they fail to understand is that unless the member of staff has a medical problem which requires treatment and possible subsequent time off work, they are unlikely to talk about any incident which may have happened outside working hours. However, this does not prevent them from having what to them are abnormal reactions which cannot be explained away easily. These reactions will sooner or later have adverse consequences and the job will suffer.

Many working hours may be lost through lack of recognition that a problem exists which, without some form of intervention, will continue to prevent the individual from achieving top performance in the job.

It frequently comes to light through gentle probing that family relationships are under pressure which then have an adverse effect on job performance. This could cause dangerously low concentration levels where the safety of others is put to risk. For example, in multi-tasking work where concentration levels have to be at the highest peak, thoughts about family issues which tend to invade the mind can cause serious lapse of concentration.

Research has shown that reduction of anxiety levels can be achieved by providing the workforce with information-based workshops to prepare for any incidents which might produce trauma. Should an incident happen in the workplace which not only involves people in the immediate vicinity but also colleagues and others who learn about the incident by word of mouth, the reactions could be far worse if the work-force are not prepared for such eventualities. It may well take some considerable time for professional help to take over and deal with crisis intervention.

At this point, any traumatised person will be unable to make decisions, or put into perspective what has just occurred. Since it is vital to provide quick, practical support for those affected, the organisation would benefit greatly by appointing suitable support staff, chosen from the workforce and trained by professionals. This support staff will be able to act as a 'prop', or carer, provide Psychological First Aid and prevent the traumatised individual from slipping into a more stressful state.

Members of the community not employed as a member of staff in a company and therefore unable to benefit from such organised care, who have been involved in a critical incident which might give rise to traumatic stress reactions, or find themselves recalling past traumatic experiences, should not try to bottle it up in the hope that it will go away again.

Such people must make the decision to find support, either by seeing their GP or finding someone with whom they can share their experiences and who will lend an empathic ear.

For those people who have read this book and feel that they can offer survivors of critical incidents a carer's support, rendering first aid cover to those who have sustained minor injuries and take care of, or enlist the services of another carer, should offer their services to their employers or make management aware that this kind of support is essential to the well being of the whole company. Those who feel that they can help the community if such incidents occur, are well advised to obtain the right training.

Lending a helping hand is part of a carer's job – this does not include counselling skills – and the characteristics required are training and knowledge in the skills of first aid, an empathetic nature, good listening skills and a calm and soothing attitude towards the person suffering from traumatic stress reactions.

Training in all these skills is available in many places and those who are willing and able to provide the right skills should make every effort to obtain the knowledge. This can be done either through their own employers or through organisations who specialise in the teaching of caring for those suffering from the reactions of traumatic stress.